Book J

# LANGUAGE Power

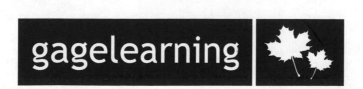

gagelearning

Nelson
1120 Birchmount Road, Toronto, Ontario, M1K 5G4
1-800-668-0671
www.nelson.com

Editorial Team: Chelsea Donaldson, Evelyn Maksimovich
Cover Adaptation: Christine Dandurand

ISBN-13: **978-0-7715-1044-1**
ISBN-10: **0-7715-1044-6**

15 16 17 18   25 24 23 22
Printed in Canada

# Table of Contents

## Unit 6  Research and Study Skills

## Final Review

# Lesson 1

## Word Origins

The English language spoken today developed over thousands of years. Some important early influences on modern English are described below.

- **Old English** Many simple one-syllable English words are derived from this Germanic language, originally spoken by peoples who invaded Britain in the fifth century C.E.

    EXAMPLES: arm, be, cow, earth, father, hate, house, love, mother

- **Old Norse** In the eighth and ninth centuries, Viking invaders also made contributions to the language.

    EXAMPLES: birth, cake, egg, gap, rag, skill, sky, want

- **French** French was the official language of Britain from the Norman Conquest (1066) until the fourteenth century. Many words related to government, the arts, and courtly life were introduced by French-speaking conquerors.

    EXAMPLES: parliament, courage, judge, jury, court, royal, grace

    (**Note:** Since French is derived from Latin, many of these words are also listed as having Latin origins. The word *court*, for example, is derived from Old French *cort*, which is in turn derived from Latin *cohors*.)

- **Latin and Greek** These classical languages influenced the development of English at several stages. Monks first introduced some religious Latin and Greek words as early as the sixth century. Under the Normans, Latin was used in churches, universities, and law courts. Finally, in the sixteenth century, a new wave of Latin and Greek words, especially those related to science and medicine, were introduced into the language by Renaissance scholars.

    EXAMPLES: **Latin:** sacred, college, study, legal, infection, virus
    **Greek:** analyse, bishop, diagnosis, geology, physiology, psalm

**A.** **Based only on the Information and examples in the box above, label the following groups of words according to the language from which each is derived: Old English (OE), Old Norse (ON), Old French (OF), Latin (L), and Greek (GK). Do not use a dictionary for this activity.**

1. divinity, medicine, student, university _____

2. anatomy, geometry, prognosis, psychology _____

3. courtesy, dance, duchess, government _____

4. bag, gape, skirt, troll _____

5. brother, dog, stone, truth _____

- Most dictionaries list word origins in brackets at the end of the definition or main entry. If a word has links to more than one language (for example, Latin and French), these other languages will also be listed, often using an abbreviation: L for Latin, OE for Old English, and so on. Check the list of abbreviations provided in the dictionary if you are unsure. The symbol < is sometimes used to mean "from."

    EXAMPLE: **college** ME < OF *colege* < L *collegium* < *collega* (Middle English, from Old French *colege*, from Latin *collegium*, from *collega*)

**B.** Using a dictionary that lists word origins, find and add one word to each group of words in Part A. For each new word, record the complete etymology (word origins) given in the dictionary. (Hint: Look for words that are related in subject matter to the words listed in Part A.)

1. _____

2. _____

3. _____

4. _____

5. _____

> ■ Since the fifteenth century, English has been adopting new words from virtually every language in the world. As a result, modern English contains a remarkably rich vocabulary.
>
> EXAMPLES: coyote (Mexican Spanish; Nahuatl *koyotl*)
> pita (Hebrew)
> walrus (Dutch *walros*; *wal(vis)* whale + *ros horse*)

**C.** Use a dictionary to find the origin of the following words. List all source languages given for each word.

1. yogurt _____

2. tornado _____

3. shampoo _____

4. sofa _____

5. tycoon _____

6. sauna _____

7. ketchup _____

8. freight _____

9. fresco _____

10. bagel _____

> ■ Canadian English has acquired words from Canadian French and Aboriginal languages.
>
> EXAMPLES: **Canadian French Words:** lacrosse, tourtière
> **Aboriginal Words:** caribou, kayak, skunk

**D.** Look up the following words in a Canadian dictionary. Find the meaning(s) identified as specifically Canadian, and then list the language of origin.

1. tuque _____

2. muskeg _____

3. potlatch _____

4. travois _____

5. inukshuk _____

# Lesson 2

## Scientific and Technical Vocabulary

> - Advances in technology and science over the last 200 years or so have led to the introduction of many new words. Understanding how such words are formed can help increase your understanding of their meaning. Many of these words were formed by using Latin and Greek roots, prefixes, and suffixes, either alone or in combination.
>
>   EXAMPLE: television (Greek *tele*, meaning "far" + Latin *videre*, meaning "see")

**A. Use a dictionary to find the Latin or Greek word(s) used to form each of the following words.**

1. astronaut _____
2. clone _____
3. nuclear _____
4. vaccine _____
5. oxygen _____
6. peripheral _____

> - Technical words can also be formed by combining letters or words to create a new word.
>
>   EXAMPLE: Canadarm (Canada + arm)
>
> - Still other words are formed by adding a new meaning to an existing word.
>
>   EXAMPLE: (computer) virus

**B. Identify the word combinations used to create the following terms. Use a dictionary, if necessary.**

1. modem _____
2. laser _____
3. e-zine _____
4. radar _____
5. sonar _____
6. scuba _____

**C. For each term below, record the first meaning listed in the dictionary. Then, write the definition that corresponds to the scientific or technical usage of the word.**

1. interface (first meaning) _____

   (computer usage) _____

2. satellite (first meaning) _____

   (space technology usage) _____

3. facsimile (first meaning) _____

   (technology usage) _____

# Lesson 3

## Roots, Prefixes, and Suffixes

> - **Root words** can be familiar English words or word forms derived from other languages, especially Latin and Greek. Root words can be combined with prefixes, suffixes, or sometimes with other root words.
>   EXAMPLE: The Greek roots *psyche* (meaning "mind") and *logos* (meaning "study") give us <u>psychology</u>, "the study of the mind."

**A.** For each root word, think of two more examples of English words that come from the same root. Add these words to the last column.

| Greek Root | Meaning | English Forms | English Examples |
|---|---|---|---|
| **1.** bios | life | -bio- | biology, biopsy, _____ |
| **2.** dynamis | power | -dyna- | dynamic, dynamo, _____ |
| **3.** geo | earth | -geo- | geography, geometry, _____ |
| **4.** logos | word, study | -log-, -logy- | geology, logic, _____ |
| **5.** metron | measure | -meter-, -metr- | metre, thermometer, _____ |
| **6.** neos | new, young | -neo- | neon, neonatal, _____ |
| **7.** pathos | suffering, feeling, disease | -path- | naturopath, telepathy, _____ |
| **8.** philos | loving | -phil-, -phile- | philanthropy, philharmonic, _____ |
| **9.** phobos | panic, fear | -phob-, -phobe- | claustrophobia, phobia, _____ |
| **10.** phone | sound | -phon-, -phone- | phonic, telephone, _____ |
| **11.** pyr, pyros | fire | -pyr- | pyre, pyromania, _____ |
| **12.** techne | art | -techn- | technical, technique, _____ |
| **13.** telos | far | -tele- | telepathy, television, _____ |

**B.** Match each word to the definition that most closely fits the meaning of the word's root(s).

| | | |
|---|---|---|
| **1.** neologism | | fear of fire |
| **2.** dynamometer | | device for rockets that takes measurements and transmits them over long distances to a recording station |
| **3.** pyrophobia | | instrument for measuring force or power |
| **4.** telemeter | | a new word |
| **5.** biotechnology | | the use of living organisms to make industrial goods |
| **6.** geophone | | the study of the nature and causes of disease |
| **7.** pathology | | device that records vibrations within the earth |

**C.** For each root word, think of two more examples of English words that come from the same root. Add these words to the last column.

| Latin Root | Meaning | English Forms | English Examples |
|---|---|---|---|
| **1.** alter | other | -alt-, -ulter- | adulterate, altercation, _____ |
| **2.** canere, cantare | to sing, chant | -cant-, -chant- | cantata, chant, _____ |
| **3.** capere | to take, grasp | -cap-, -ceive-, -cept-, -cip- | capable, conceive, _____ |
| **4.** currere | to run | -course-, -cur- | course, current, _____ |
| **5.** dicere | to say | -dic-, -dict- | dictate, diction, _____ |
| **6.** finire | to end, limit | -fin-, -fine- | fine, finish, _____ |
| **7.** jacere | to throw, to lie | -jac-, -ject- | adjacent, project, _____ |
| **8.** malus | bad, evil, wrong | -mal- | malevolent, malice, _____ |
| **9.** mater | mother (female) | -mater-, -matr- | maternal, matriarch, _____ |
| **10.** pater | father | -pater-, -patr- | paternal, patriarch, _____ |
| **11.** pellere | to drive or beat | -pel-, -puls- | compel, pulsate, _____ |
| **12.** scribere | to write | -scrib-, -script- | scribe, script, _____ |
| **13.** trahere | to draw | -tract- | contract, subtract, _____ |
| **14.** turbare | to disturb | -turb- | disturb, turbo, _____ |
| **15.** venire | to come | -ven-, -venue- | convention, revenue, _____ |

---

■ A **prefix** is a syllable or word added to the beginning of a root word to change its meaning.

| EXAMPLES: | |
|---|---|
| **a-, an-** | without; not |
| **ante-** | before; earlier |
| **anti-** | against; opposed to; preventing; relieving |
| **de-** | remove; do the opposite of; down; away; cause to leave something; entirely |
| **dys-** | bad; abnormal |
| **il-, im-, in-, ir-** | not; in |
| **inter-** | together; between; among |
| **mis-** | wrong; wrongly; bad; badly |
| **un-** | not |

---

**D.** **Complete the following sentences using words from the box below. The definitions in italics provide clues to the correct prefix.**

| unregulated | mislabelled | amoral | deregulated | unlabelled | immoral |
|---|---|---|---|---|---|

1. Some observers say that the electricity market should remain under government control, because prices would soar in a[n] _____ market. *[having regulations removed from]*

2. _____ sport fishing has wiped out fish stocks in the river. *[not governed by regulations]*

3. The lab technician _____ my blood sample, so I got someone else's results. *[wrongly labelled]*

4. I wonder what is inside that _____ can on the shelf. *[not labelled]*

5. You know that it is wrong to steal, so it would be _____ for you to do so. *[not moral]*

6. You can't blame the lion for killing its prey, because nature is _____. *[without a moral sense; not governed by morality]*

**E.** **Use the definition given in parentheses to determine the correct prefix for each of the following words.**

1. _____ function (failure to function normally)

2. _____ heroic (opposed to heroism)

3. _____ terminable (endless)

4. _____ mediary (a go-between)

5. _____ cedent (previous thing or event)

6. _____ orexia (chronic loss of appetite)

---

- A **suffix** is an ending added to a word, which changes its meaning or function in the sentence. It may also change the spelling of the original word.

  EXAMPLES: teach (verb) + er = teacher (noun)
  sterile (adjective) + ize = sterilize (verb)
  book (noun) + ish = bookish (adjective)

---

**F.** **Fill in all the blank spaces in the following chart by adding appropriate suffixes to each word.**

| Verb | Noun | Adjective |
|---|---|---|
| convene | | |
| prescribe | | |
| divide | | |
| arrange | | |
| | apology | |
| | | soft |
| | | deviant |
| | | diverse |

## Standard and Non-Standard English

- When addressing an audience in a formal situation or submitting written work at school, it is not always appropriate to use the same words and expressions that you would choose when talking informally with a group of friends.
- **Standard Canadian English** refers to the language used and accepted by educated individuals as appropriate for any situation. Standard Canadian English can be formal or informal; however, it does not include slang words.
- **Non-standard English** is called **slang**. This type of language comes in and goes out of fashion quickly, so it is not always found in dictionaries. However, some slang words are included in the dictionary. They are usually labelled *slang* or *non-standard*.
- Slang is not usually considered acceptable in formal speech or writing, and should be used sparingly, if at all, even in informal writing.

**A. Find seven slang words or expressions in the following passage and replace them with more formal words or expressions. Use proofreader's marks to make the changes.**

Stanley Milgram was a shrink. In the 1960s, he performed a controversial experiment in which subjects were told they were taking part in research to discover the effects of punishment on learning. The subjects were ordered to administer shocks to a "learner" every time the learner goofed on a memory test. The shocks increased in strength with each mistake. Unbeknownst to the subjects, the learner was actually an actor, and no shock was actually delivered. However, as the intensity of the shocks appeared to increase, the reaction of the actor became more and more hairy. He or she would call out, scream, even beg to be let go.

Milgram found that an astonishing number of subjects continued to zap the actor, although they believed they were causing real pain or distress. Very few chickened out, apparently because they did not want to make waves by defying authority.

The people in Milgram's experiment were ordinary joes, just like you and me. How do you think you would react in a similar situation?

**B. Write three other slang expressions you know that would be inappropriate in most written work (no profanities or swear words). Then, give the meaning of each expression.**

1. _____

2. _____

3. _____

# Lesson 5 — Canadian Spelling

- Canadian spelling follows both British and American conventions. Often, two spellings of the same word will be listed as correct in the dictionary. For example, you will probably find entries for both color and colour in a Canadian dictionary. However, the color entry will refer you to the entry given for the preferred spelling, colour.

    EXAMPLE: **color, colorant, coloration** See COLOUR.

- In general, the first spelling listed in an entry is considered preferable.

    EXAMPLE: **colour** or **color** (In this dictionary, colour is the preferred spelling, so it is listed first.)

- When you have a choice between two different spellings, be consistent in your choices. For example, while color and colour are both used in Canada, you should not use both spellings in the same piece of writing. Choose one form and use it consistently. If you use colour, then use the -our ending for all other words with similar endings, such as labour and neighbour.

**A.** Complete the third column using the preferred spellings given in a Canadian dictionary.

| Category | American | Canadian | British |
|---|---|---|---|
| **-or** or **-our** ending | color | | colour |
| | labor | | labour |
| | neighbor | | neighbour |
| | savor | | savour |
| **-er** or **-re** ending | center | | centre |
| | liter | | litre |
| | meter | | metre |
| | theater | | theatre |
| **-se** or **-ce** ending | defense | | defence |
| | license | | licence (n), license (v) |
| | practise | | practice (n), practise (v) |
| **-yze** or **-yse** ending | analyze | | analyse |
| | paralyze | | paralyse |
| **silent -e + suffix** | acknowledgment | | acknowledgement |
| | judgment | | judgement |
| | likable | | likeable |
| **l, m,** or **p + suffix** | canceled | | cancelled |
| | diagramed | | diagrammed |
| | jewelry | | jewellery |
| | worshiped | | worshipped |
| **miscellaneous** | burned | | burnt |
| | catalog | | catalogue |
| | check (bill) | | cheque |
| | civilization | | civilisation |
| | gray | | grey |
| | maneuver | | manoeuvre |
| | program | | programme |

**B.** **Edit the following passage so that the spelling is consistent with the preferred Canadian spellings in the chart on the previous page.**

There we were, away from civilisation and the clamor of everyday life. The three of us—Marco, Dave, and I— were spending a weekend in the wilderness. When we arrived, the sky looked gray, but we didn't stop to analyze what that might mean; we figured we could handle whatever came our way. It wasn't until we heard an ominous rumbling that we questioned our judgement. The rain began to pelt down on us as we hammered tent pegs into the ground.

We spent a miserable night, but the clear, bright morning revived our spirits. Marco and I prepared breakfast. It didn't matter that the toast was burnt, the eggs rubbery, and the coffee lukewarm; we savored every mouthful, because we had made it ourselves.

The next day, we hiked through the woods and visited an interpretive center, which had some interesting facts about the local wildlife. I was surprised to discover that rattlesnakes had been spotted within a few kilometers of our camp.

In the evening, we returned to the tranquility of our campsite. We cooked wieners over the fire and heated a pot of beans. As it grew dark, we swapped stories and Dave made us sing a few old campfire songs from our days as Boy Scouts. We were definitely out of practise, though.

Tired from hiking, we crawled into our sleeping bags earlier than usual. I lay there, listening to all the little rustlings and scrapings in the woods, until I fell asleep. A loud scuffle outside the tent woke us all up. All I could think was "rattlesnake!" The scuffling stopped, and a foul odor spread through the tent. Suddenly, rattlesnakes were the farthest thing from my mind. It was worse: a skunk!

---

- Many words that end in -our omit the -u when certain suffixes are added.
  EXAMPLES: humour, humorous  BUT  honour, honourable

---

**C.** **Using a Canadian dictionary, check the spelling of the underlined words below. Write <u>C</u> if the word is spelled correctly. If it is not, write the correct spelling on the line.**

1. Sandra Shamas is one of my favourite <u>humourists</u>. _____

2. What a <u>glamorous</u> dress that is! _____

3. You need to get a <u>deodourizer</u> for your car. _____

4. It was a dull, <u>colourless</u> day. _____

5. The police officer was commended for her <u>valourous</u> actions. _____

6. I bought my nephew a <u>colouring</u> book. _____

7. <u>Colorful</u> artwork covered the walls of the gallery. _____

8. That film <u>glamourizes</u> violence. _____

---

## Denotation and Connotation

- The **denotation** of a word is its exact meaning as stated in the dictionary. The **connotation** of a word is its implied meaning, which affects the emotional impact the word has on the reader.

  EXAMPLES: The words huddle and snuggle both describe the action of drawing close together. However, huddle has a more appropriate connotation for the following sentence: The family huddled together in fear. Whereas snuggle is more appropriate in this sentence: The family snuggled together on the couch.

  To resolve to do something has a more forceful connotation than to decide.

  To gaze at the horizon has a more relaxed connotation than to peer.

  Forceful has a more positive connotation than pushy.

- When you write, consider not only the denotations of your words, but also their connotations. Choose words with connotations that fit the mood or idea you wish to convey.

**A. Underline the word in parentheses that has the most positive connotation and is best suited to the tone and context of the sentence. Use a dictionary to check the meaning of any words you do not know.**

1. Perry had a (childish, childlike, infantile) expression on his face.

2. Marcella seems very (arrogant, presumptuous, confident) about her abilities.

3. I found that sales clerk very (chatty, garrulous, communicative).

4. Arthur loves to (talk, chatter, gossip).

5. I have never seen such a[n] (impressive, flashy, ostentatious) display of wealth.

6. My great uncle has developed some (eccentric, odd, unique) views on life.

7. The authorities were (rigid, firm, unbending) in applying the rules.

**B. Underline the word with the most appropriate connotation from the choices given in parentheses. Consider the tone, mood, and intent of the writer when making your choices.**

Dear Councillor Taylor:

I am (concerned, worried, upset) by your decision to sell the lands south of the city to a developer. As you well know, these lands contain (unusual, unique, strange) (swamp, wetland) areas that are home to a rich variety of wildlife. If we continue to (erode, consume, use up) the habitat of these (creatures, beasts, critters), we will eventually (destroy, compromise, alter) our ecosystem. Instead of (exploiting, profiting from, utilizing) a[n] (natural, undeveloped, untapped) region such as this, why not preserve it as a conservation area, as was suggested by several community groups?

We expect our leaders to act with responsibility and (wisdom, knowledge, savvy), not with a view to making (a quick buck, investments, a profit) at the cost of our ecological heritage. You have failed to meet those expectations.

# Lesson 7

## Figurative Language

> - **Figurative language** (also called **figures of speech**) is language that goes beyond the literal meaning of the words to create beauty, force, or style. When used effectively and sparingly, figurative language can make ideas easier to understand. Some common figures of speech are simile, metaphor, personification, paradox, and hyperbole.
> - A **simile** is a direct comparison that is usually introduced by <u>like</u> or <u>as</u>.
>   - EXAMPLES: My cell phone is like a best friend to me.
>     She was as shy as a field mouse.
> - A **metaphor** is an implied comparison.
>   - EXAMPLE: My journal is a haven that I turn to when I am upset.
> - **Personification** is a metaphor that attributes human qualities to something that is not human.
>   - EXAMPLE: Time stood still.

**A.** **Identify the figure of speech used in each of the following quotations. Write <u>S</u> for simile, <u>M</u> for metaphor, and <u>PER</u> for personification.**

1. The family—that dear octopus from whose tentacles we never quite escape.
   —Dodie Smith, *Dear Octopus*                                               _____

2. Money doesn't talk, it swears.        —Bob Dylan, "It's Alright Ma (I'm Only Bleeding)"    _____

3. Some say a heart is just like a wheel; if you bend it, you can't mend it.
   —Kate and Anna McGarrigle, "Heart Like a Wheel"                            _____

4. Then fear, disguised in the garb of mild-mannered doubt, slips into your mind….
   —Yann Martel, *The Life of Pi*                                             _____

5. A herd of elephants…pacing along as if they had an appointment at the end of the world.
   —Isak Dinesen, *Out of Africa*                                            _____

6. The mystery of language was revealed to me. I knew then that w-a-t-e-r meant the wonderful cool something that was flowing over my hand. That living word awakened my soul, gave it light, joy, set it free!        —Helen Keller, *The Story of My Life*    _____

7. The word *bulldozer* wandered through his mind for a moment in search of something to connect with.        —Douglas Adams, *Hitchhiker's Guide to the Galaxy*    _____

8. My desire to get here [Parliament] was like miners' coal dust, it was under my fingers and I couldn't scrub it out.        —Betty Boothroyd, British Labour MP    _____

9. I think that I shall never see
   A poem lovely as a tree        —Joyce Kilmer, "Trees"                      _____

10. Our eyes locked, and someone threw away the key.        —Annie Dillard, "Living Like Weasels"    _____

**B.** **Create your own example of simile, metaphor, and personification.**

1. Simile: _____

2. Metaphor: _____

3. Personification: _____

> - A **paradox** is a statement that may be true but that seems to contradict itself.
>   EXAMPLES: Some of us are not all here.
>   The more I learn, the less I know.
> - **Hyperbole** is a statement that is exaggerated for effect.
>   EXAMPLES: I am so hungry I could eat a horse.
>   Waves as high as mountains broke over the reef.

**C. Identify the figure of speech used in each of the following quotations as <u>PAR</u> for paradox, or <u>H</u> for hyperbole.**

1. There are whole
   magazines with not much in them
   but the word love....
      —Margaret Atwood, "Variations on the Word Love"            _____

2. It was the best of times, it was the worst of times.            —Charles Dickens, *A Tale of Two Cities*   _____

3. Please accept my resignation. I don't want to belong to any club that would
   accept me as a member.     —Groucho Marx, *Groucho and Me*            _____

4. I loved Ophelia. Forty-thousand brothers could not with all their quantity of love
   Make up the difference.     —William Shakespeare, *Hamlet*            _____

> - When using figurative language in your own writing, be careful not to mix your
>   metaphors. A mixed metaphor combines two or more different images that
>   are not compatible.
>   EXAMPLE: **Mixed Metaphor:** The character is reduced to a pawn in a giant
>   chess game, crawling like an insect toward her inevitable end.
>   [the image of the pawn and the insect are incompatible]
>   **Revised:** The character is reduced to a pawn in a giant chess
>   game, moved by some invisible hand toward her inevitable end.
>   [continues the chess metaphor]
>   **Revised:** The character is reduced to a helpless insect, crawling
>   toward her inevitable end. [continues the insect metaphor]

**D. Correct the following mixed metaphors by eliminating one of the images. Replace it with a compatible image or with non-figurative language.**

1. As he spins his web of lies, he is planting the seeds of his own destruction.

   _____

2. He knew he was treading on thin ice, but he sailed onward, undaunted.

   _____

3. Karla took the wind out of my sails by throwing cold water on my plans.

   _____

# *Lesson* 8 — Clichés, Jargon, and Redundant Language

- When making word choices in your writing, take care to avoid clichés, jargon, and redundant language.
- **Clichés** are overused expressions—often similes or metaphors—that have lost their original impact.
  - EXAMPLES: She's <u>as honest as the day is long</u>.
  - He crept <u>like a thief in the night</u>.
- Unless you are sure of your ability to write fresh, original expressions, it is often best to simplify clichés, or omit them.

**A.** **Suggest a more vivid image to replace each of the following clichés.**

**1.** as hard as rock _____

**2.** make a mountain out of a molehill _____

**3.** busy as a beaver _____

**4.** stubborn as a mule _____

**5.** wouldn't hurt a fly _____

**6.** gentle as a lamb _____

**7.** sell like hotcakes _____

**8.** light as a feather _____

**9.** beat around the bush _____

**10.** take the bull by the horns _____

**B.** **Underline the clichéd expression(s) in each of the following sentences. Then, rewrite the sentences to eliminate or revise the clichés.**

**1.** When it comes to saving money, it's best to make hay while the sun shines.

_____

**2.** Justin always gives 110 percent to any project he takes on.

_____

**3.** The bottom line is, your eyes were bigger than your stomach.

_____

**4.** Without my glasses, I am as blind as a bat.

_____

**5.** When we found ourselves in hot water, everyone started avoiding us like the plague.

- **Jargon** often refers to writing that attempts to sound important or authoritative by using unnecessary or elaborate words and phrases. Sentences containing jargon are usually long and complicated. Avoid jargon by choosing simple, straightforward language that expresses your ideas clearly.

  EXAMPLE: **Jargon:** Each team must endeavour to attain the optimum number of points in order to accomplish a victory against the opposing teams.

  **Revised:** Each team must try to get the most points to win.

- **Redundant language** refers to words or phrases that are unnecessary or repeat what has already been said. For example, the expression <u>at this point in time</u> is redundant. Both <u>at this point</u> and <u>at this time</u> convey the same message more concisely (and <u>now</u> is even more concise!).

- To eliminate both jargon and redundant language, choose simple words over difficult ones, and use as few words as possible to express your ideas.

**C. Revise the following letter by replacing the ten examples of jargon (in boldface) with simpler expressions. Then, find and eliminate fifteen examples of redundant language. Use proofreader's marks to indicate your changes.**

Dear Sir:

I **would like to express my disagreement** with your recent editorial "What Is Wrong with Young People Today?" in which the writer **makes the assertion** that "Young people do not seem to care about politics the way we did in the 1960s."

In my opinion, I think this statement is based on stereotypes, not on true facts. Apparently, it seems that the author has had **an inadequate amount of** actual contact with young people. I am an eighteen-year-old who **has an involvement in** many numerous political causes. I know **a large number of** other young people who, like me, are **endeavouring** to make their voices heard. We care deeply about our planet and about our society that we live in. What's more, we are also willing to **utilize** our time and energy to **effectuate change in** the problems left to us by previous generations who came before us.

If the writer has not noticed our involvement, the reason is probably because we are often overpowered by the voices of our elders. Youth in the 1960s were able to **strategize** and carry out social change because their sheer mass gave them power that we no longer have any more. Today the baby-boom generation is older now, and so therefore our society is aging, too. The end result is that young people have **a greater degree of** difficulty making their voices heard. But we care very much, though, about what lies ahead of us in the future. If only the author who wrote that editorial had taken the time to listen a little more closely, he or she would have heard a passionate cry for justice rising up from the young.

Yours truly,

Kyla Weinstein

# Lesson 9

## Commonly Confused Words

- Words that have similar spellings or pronunciations are often confused in writing. When proofreading your work, pay particular attention to the spelling and meaning of the words below.

  | | | |
  |---|---|---|
  | accept, except | loose, lose | their, there, they're |
  | advice, advise | passed, past | to, too, two |
  | choose, chose | principal, principle | weather, whether |
  | complement, compliment | | |

**A. Choose the correct word to complete the sentence.**

1. I would (advice, advise) you to turn back.

2. (Their, There, They're) coming on Monday to fix the plumbing.

3. Where did you (loose, lose) your wallet?

4. This road is (to, too, two) slippery to bicycle on.

5. What is the (weather, whether) like today?

6. We (passed, past) that car a few kilometres back, didn't we?

7. A silk scarf would (complement, compliment) that outfit perfectly.

8. The case dissolved when the (principal, principle) witness refused to testify.

9. Did you (choose, chose) to pay extra for air conditioning in your car?

10. Everyone went home (accept, except) Joey and Hedya.

- **already** means "previously": The bus has already left.
  **all ready** means "a state of readiness": Your car is all ready to go.
- **altogether** means "completely": I want to forget about it altogether.
  **all together** means "in a group": The files were all together in a drawer.
- **anymore** refers to time: Walt doesn't come here anymore.
  **any more** refers to quantity: I can't eat any more.
- **awhile** is an adverb: Rest here awhile.
  **a while** is a noun phrase: Rest for a while.   OR   A while later....
- **into** generally shows direction or movement: They moved into the house.
  **in** usually indicates location (i.e., not out). You'll have to come in to discuss this problem.

**B. Choose the correct word in parentheses.**

1. (Altogether, All together), they heaved and pushed the mattress up the stairs.

2. Do you take Japanese language courses (anymore, any more)?

3. I am (all ready, already) nervous, and my presentation isn't until tomorrow!

4. They said they would call me in (awhile, a while).

5. Jasmine marched (into, in to) the room.

**A.** Identify the language of origin for each word below. Use the information introduced in Lesson 1. Don't use a dictionary.

**1.** legal, student _____

**2.** scrap, Viking _____

**3.** painting, chivalry _____

**4.** axe, child _____

**5.** hymn, geology _____

**B.** Use a dictionary to find the origin of the following words.

**1.** chipmunk _____

**2.** typhoon _____

**3.** bit (computers) _____

**4.** loot _____

**5.** cola _____

**6.** khaki _____

**7.** schnitzel _____

**8.** judo _____

**9.** mukluk _____

**10.** mosquito _____

**C.** Match the words below with the correct definition. Use the information from Lesson 3 about Greek and Latin roots. Underline the word in the definition that corresponds to the meaning of the root.

**1.** biomass            confused or disturbed

**2.** geostationary            female ruler or head

**3.** matriarch            a body in space that emits a regular beat of radio waves

**4.** pathogen            moving at the same speed as earth

**5.** pulsar            the total amount of living organisms in a given area

**6.** turbid            a disease-causing agent

**D.** Add the correct prefix to fit the definition given in parentheses.

**1.** _____ rhythmia (abnormal rhythm)

**2.** _____ attractive (not attractive)

**3.** _____ convulsant (substance that prevents convulsions)

**4.** _____ fog (remove the fog from)

**5.** _____ flate (do the opposite of inflate)

**6.** _____ planetary (between the planets)

**E.** For each of the following words, add a suffix to change the word to the part of speech indicated in parentheses.

1. predict + _____ = _____ (noun)

2. attract + _____ = _____ (adjective)

3. colony + _____ = _____ (verb)

4. compel + _____ = _____ (noun)

**F.** Underline all the words that are misspelled or that do not follow standard Canadian spelling conventions. Write the revised spelling above the word.

1. The principle complemented Carmen on winning honorable mention for her speech "Learning from

   Passed Mistakes."

2. When we were in the dessert, we always traveled in pairs so we wouldn't loose our way.

3. I'm going to watch my favorite TV programme weather you're their or not.

4. My advise is to chose a doctor who has a license to practice medicine.

**G.** Replace each underlined word with a synonym that has a more positive connotation. (You may have to change other words to make the sentence work.)

1. The cake was smeared with icing.

2. The speaker lectured the group on the correct way to write a memo.

3. The boy snivelled for hours over his lost cat.

4. She dug her fingers into the heavy, brown dirt in the flower bed.

5. Please stop snooping in my desk.

**H.** Identify the figure of speech in each of the following sentences as simile (S), metaphor (M), personification (PER), paradox (PAR), or hyperbole (H).

1. Fear walked beside her through the alley. _____

2. Outside my window, the backyard was a snowy canvas, not yet painted. _____

3. His beady eyes were as black as coal. _____

4. In some cases, the cure can be worse than the disease. _____

5. He looked at me with a face that was older than time itself. _____

---

**Read the passage below, and then answer the questions that follow.**

[Paragraph 1] Ernest Shackleton is perhaps the most triumphant failure in the history of world exploration. The story of Shackleton's attempt to cross the Antarctic is an inspiring account of valiant struggle and subsistence against all odds.

[Paragraph 2] Shackleton and his crew sailed for the Antarctic on a ship called *The Endurance* in December 1914. But before they could reach land, the ship became trapped in pack ice. They remained stuck for ten long months; eventually they were forced to abandon ship as the ice made mincemeat of *The Endurance*. They now found themselves in a real pickle. Alone, with few supplies, and no hope of rescue, they camped for five months on ice floes, moving frequently as the ice shifted beneath them.

[Paragraph 3] Luckily, they had managed to salvage three small lifeboats. With the ice breaking up around them, they took to the boats and made safe harbour at a place called Elephant Island. But they were out of the frying pan and into the fire; the island was uninhabited, and no ships were likely to pass near it. Shackleton decided they're only hope was to try to make it to South Georgia Island, where there was a whaling station. Leaving most of the crew behind, Shackleton and five others set off in bitterly cold whether on a hopeless 1300-kilometer voyage, across frozen, inhospitable seas, in a small lifeboat. At one point during the terrifying journey, a giant wave reared up in front of them like a wall of water. They gave themselves up for lost and braced for the impact. But although they were soaked to the bone, the boat survived, and, after some frantic bailing, stayed afloat.

[Paragraph 4] After seventeen days, they reached South Georgia Island. This was an incredible accomplishment. However, they did not have much time to congratulate themselves. They had landed on the wrong side of the island, and the only way to the whaling station was across uncharted 1400-metre-high mountains and glaciers. Shackleton ordered three men to stay behind, and set off with two others on the last leg of their jaunt. When they finally arrived at the station, the first people they met were two young boys from a whaling ship, who looked at the three strangers before running away in terror. And no wonder: Shackleton and his men had been traveling for months. They were unshaved, unwashed, and had not had a change of clothes in almost a year!

[Paragraph 5] As soon as he could, Shackleton returned for the men he had left behind. Incredibly, each and every one of the men left on Elephant Island and back at the original base camp was found alive. The Shackleton expedition did not succeed in its original task of reaching the South Pole, but it is considered by many to be a triumph, however. The reason is because, accept for one man who lost a few toes to frostbite, not one member of the valourous crew was harmed during the whole entire ordeal.

A. Find the three words in Paragraph 1 that have a prefix, root, and suffix. Using a dictionary, fill in the chart below with the meaning of the prefix and the root word. Identify what part of speech the suffix forms. Complete the chart by adding another word with the same root.

| Word in Paragraph 1 | Prefix and Meaning | Root and Meaning | Suffix (Part of Speech) | Related Word |
|---|---|---|---|---|
| 1. | | | | |
| 2. | | | | |
| 3. | | | | |

B. Identify and record below two informal expressions in Paragraph 2. Then, suggest a more formal replacement for each.

1. _____     _____

2. _____     _____

C. Underline two clichéd expressions in Paragraph 3. On the lines below, state whether each is an example of simile, metaphor, or hyperbole. Then, revise the paragraph to eliminate these clichés. Use proofreader's marks to incorporate your changes.

1. cliché #1: _____ is an example of _____

2. cliché #2: _____ is an example of _____

D. Find synonyms with more appropriate connotations for the two underlined words in Paragraph 4.

1. synonyms for "jaunt": _____

2. synonyms for "looked": _____

E. Find four examples of redundancy in Paragraph 5. Use proofreader's marks to eliminate them.

F. Find one paradoxical statement in the passage. Write it on the line below.

_____

G. Circle three commonly confused words that are misspelled in the passage and three words that are not spelled according to Canadian conventions. Correct the spelling of each word using proofreader's marks.

# Subjects and Predicates

> ■ Every sentence contains a simple subject, which is a noun or pronoun, and a simple predicate, which is a verb.
>
> EXAMPLES: **Simple Subject**  **Simple Predicate**
> People            listened
> Canadians         are
>
> ■ In commands, the simple subject is usually not stated, but <u>you</u> is the implied subject.
>
> EXAMPLE:  (You) Wait.
>
> ■ Some sentences are composed of the simple subject and simple predicate alone. However, most sentences contain words that modify these basic elements. The **complete subject** includes the simple subject and all the words that modify it. The **complete predicate** includes the simple predicate and all the words that modify it.
>
> EXAMPLES: **Complete Subject**       **Complete Predicate**
> The people at the concert   listened silently to the performance.
> Most Canadians              are hockey fans.

**A.  Draw a vertical line between the complete subject and predicate. Then, underline and label the simple subject SS and the simple predicate SP. If the subject is implied, underline only the simple predicate.**

1. The root system of that plant is very strong and well established.

2. The weather at this time of year changes quickly.

3. Take a few moments to catch your breath.

4. All of the people sitting in the front row of the auditorium screamed.

5. The Internet has made research much easier and more accessible.

6. The article on the front page of the newspaper depressed me.

7. Timothy Findley, one of Canada's best-loved writers, died in France.

8. Those jeans need to be shortened by about seven centimetres.

9. We are going with Pat to buy a new outfit for next Saturday night.

10. Those application forms have not been filled out properly.

11. Bring these CDs over to Marika's house.

12. Your new assignment is on the board.

**B.  Add words to the simple subjects and predicates below to create your own sentences. Underline the complete subject once, and the complete predicate twice.**

1. car/stolen _____

2. Ray/chose _____

3. waves/helps _____

4. papers/blew _____

5. climbers/reached _____

- Usually, the subject comes before the predicate. However, many questions place the subject between two parts of the verb. (Subjects are in bold type; predicates are in italics.)

    EXAMPLES: *Can* **you** *see*?   *Will* **Shanthy** *win*?

- In most sentences that begin with <u>there</u> or <u>it</u> plus a linking verb (usually a form of <u>be</u>), the subject comes after the verb. In these cases, <u>there</u> or <u>it</u> is not counted as part of the subject or the predicate. To find the real subject, try rephrasing the sentence without <u>there</u> or <u>it</u>. The word that becomes the subject of the new sentence is also the subject of the original sentence.

    EXAMPLES: There *is* a **restaurant** up ahead. [= A **restaurant** *is* up ahead.]
    There *are* **holes** in my socks. [= **Holes** *are* in my socks.]
    It *is* fun **to make** salsa. [= **To make** salsa *is* fun.]
    It *can be* tricky **balancing** school and work. [= **Balancing** school and work *can be* tricky.]

- Other sentences place part of the predicate before the subject. This construction tends to sound old fashioned or formal.

    EXAMPLES: Never *have* **I** *been* so *enchanted* by a theatrical production!
    At the top of the hill *stood* **the war monument**.

**C.** **Underline the simple subject once and the simple predicate twice in the following sentences.**

1. What are you doing after class?

2. Beneath the solid surface of the earth lies a hot, molten liquid core.

3. There are books lying everywhere in her office.

4. Across the empty sky passed a group of white clouds.

5. It is easy to make a video with the right equipment.

- <u>There</u> or <u>it</u> plus a linking verb is called an **expletive**. Too many expletive sentences can make your writing wordy and dull. Whenever possible, replace expletives with more concise constructions.

    EXAMPLES: **Expletive:** There are only two planets closer than Earth to the sun.
    **Revised:** Only two planets are closer than Earth to the sun.

    **Expletive:** It is unfair to let some students out early.
    **Revised:** Letting some students out early is unfair.

**D.** **Reword the expletive constructions in the following passage so that the subject precedes the verb. Use proofreader's marks to make the necessary changes. In the space provided, explain how the tone of the writing has been changed.**

There are a number of people who have indicated an interest in an end-of-year graduation party. However, it is not easy preparing such a gathering all alone. Perhaps there should be three working teams set up: one to order food and drinks, one to rent a hall, and one to advertise the event. There are fifteen people who have agreed to help out, so each group would have five people. There is a student in the other class who is a professional DJ. Perhaps she could provide the music. There will probably be other tasks coming up, which we will assign as we go along. It is a good idea ending the year this way! **[7 changes]**

> - A **compound subject** is made up of two or more subjects that share the same predicate. The two parts of the subject are usually joined together by <u>and</u> or <u>or</u>.
>
>   compound subject   predicate     compound subject   predicate
>   EXAMPLE:  **Harry and Sam** are brothers.  **Shaheen or Hong** will read for us.
>
> - A **compound predicate** consists of two or more verbs that share the same subject. The two verbs are usually linked together by <u>and</u>, <u>or</u>, or <u>but</u>.
>
>   *compound predicate*
>   EXAMPLE:  **Amina** *looked* at me *and laughed*.
>
>   *compound predicate*
>   **Tara** *likes* chocolate *but hates* vanilla.
>
> - Some sentences have a compound subject and a compound predicate.
>
>   compound subject   *compound predicate*
>   EXAMPLE:  **Harry and Sam** *looked* at me *and laughed*.

**E.** Underline the complete subject once and the complete predicate twice in the following sentences. Write <u>CS</u> above the subject if it is compound, and <u>CP</u> above the predicate if it is compound. (Remember, expletives such as <u>there</u> or <u>it</u> are not counted as part of the subject or the predicate.)

1. Swimming and weight-lifting provide a complete physical workout.

2. Standing in the cold without wearing mitts and then warming my hands before the fire makes my fingers throb.

3. People came from Halifax and the surrounding areas to watch the Canadian Junior Hockey Championships.

4. Roberta or Dennis will mow the lawn and trim the hedges and vines.

5. Zoltan always arrives first and leaves after everyone else.

6. When can we start the video again?

7. Mei or I will be along shortly to collect your application forms.

8. There are seven forks missing from the cutlery drawer.

9. Louder and louder grew the sound of hoofbeats.

10. It is difficult getting a scholarship to that school.

11. How does the DVD player work?

12. Cards and letters arrived daily during Jan's hospital stay, but were left unread.

13. Risa and Marco work at the same restaurant and play in a band together.

14. Volunteers at the hospital gain personal fulfillment as well as valuable experience.

15. There is no froth on my cappuccino.

16. Hold this to your mouth and breathe in.

17. The owner of those two Rottweilers gives them lots of exercise but never takes them off the leash.

## Direct Objects

> - Sometimes, a verb in the predicate requires a noun or pronoun to complete its meaning. This is known as the **direct object** of the verb.
> - A direct object tells who or what receives the action of the verb. Words or phrases that modify the noun or pronoun are also considered part of the direct object.
>     EXAMPLES: James collected (what?) **signatures on the petition**.
>         [on the petition modifies the noun signatures]
>     My umbrella protected (whom?) **me**.
> - Understanding direct objects will help you when you are constructing sentences in the active and passive voice (see Lesson 33).

**A. Circle the noun that is functioning as a direct object in each sentence. Underline any words that modify it.**

1. The impact of the meteor left a large hole in the ground.

2. Thousands of people lined the streets.

3. Alejandra expected a much better mark than this.

4. To pay for his trip to Europe, Robert sold his stereo.

5. Avril quickly sent a message about her change of plans.

6. The old Ottawa jail now houses a popular hostel.

7. Cassie loves skiing on machine-groomed trails.

8. The west wing of the museum contains ancient Egyptian artifacts.

9. My cousin is taking belly-dancing lessons.

10. Suyin kindled the fire at the campsite.

> - The dictionary labels verbs that take a direct object **transitive**, and those that don't **intransitive**.
> - Some verbs can be transitive or intransitive, but the meaning of the verb in each case may be slightly different.
>     EXAMPLE: **Intransitive (no direct object):** Mr. Kim runs.
>         **Transitive (needs direct object):** Mr. Kim runs (what?) **the Asian grocery**.
> (Hint: If a preposition such as in, of, with, to, or for comes right after the verb, the verb is probably intransitive.)

**B. Label each verb in the following sentences transitive (T) or intransitive (I). For transitive verbs, underline the noun or pronoun that is the direct object.**

1. Under pressure, Jason eventually told the truth.

2. I can't tell this story without laughing.

3. Kyle paints beautifully and with great skill.

4. Mina painted a picture of me.

5. The hot handle burned my hand.

6. Pale skin burns more easily in the sun.

7. The vines have grown taller since last summer.

8. We grew those flowers from seeds.

9. Do you see that skiing lodge over there?

10. With these glasses I see much better.

# Indirect Objects

> - In addition to a direct object (DO), some verbs can take an **indirect object** (IO). The indirect object is a noun or pronoun that tells <u>to whom/what</u> or <u>for whom/what</u> an action is done. The indirect object is always placed between the verb and its direct object.
>
> **IO**     *DO*
> <small>EXAMPLE:</small> Jill gave **Jack** *money*.
>
> - Words or phrases that modify the noun or pronoun are also considered part of the indirect object.
>
> **IO**         *DO*
> <small>EXAMPLE:</small> Jill gave **her friend Jack** *a lot of money*.
>
> - An indirect object can be replaced by a phrase beginning with <u>to</u> or <u>for</u>. This is a useful way to determine whether a word or phrase is functioning as an indirect object.
>
> <small>EXAMPLE:</small> Jill gave [to] her friend Jack a lot of money.

**A.  Circle the noun or pronoun that functions as the indirect object. Underline any words that modify it.**

1. I will give you thirty seconds to return my lunch!

2. Tomorrow, Ato will tell the class his story about emigrating from Ghana.

3. Bill and I showed our supervisor the money in the cash register.

4. Take the woman down the street this box of clothes.

5. Will they save us a seat in the auditorium?

6. In just three days, Alicia knitted me a sweater!

7. Mrs. Hildebrandt poured her unhappy friend a cup of coffee.

8. Send your favourite person a box of chocolates for Valentine's Day!

9. The judge gave the accused person six months in jail.

10. Napoleon Bonaparte, the great general, wrote his wife Josephine many love letters.

**B.  Label the underlined word in each sentence <u>IO</u> for indirect object, or <u>DO</u> for direct object. Remember that a direct object tells <u>what</u> or <u>who</u> receives the action, and an indirect object tells <u>to whom/what</u> or <u>for whom/what</u> the action is done.**

1. Shane gave <u>Sue</u> his word, swearing never to tell her secret to anyone.

2. Our art teacher got <u>the whole class</u> tickets to the Monet exhibit.

3. Hailey and Mackenzie printed <u>a get-well card</u> for Fraser.

4. I gave <u>my computer</u> a tap on the side to make it work.

5. Mico did not treat <u>the interview</u> seriously enough.

**C.  Write five sentences in your notebook that contain both a direct and an indirect object.**

## Subject Complements

> - A **subject complement** is a noun, pronoun, or adjective that follows a linking verb (see Lesson 25 for more on linking verbs). Words or phrases that modify the noun, pronoun, or adjective are also considered part of the subject complement.
> - The subject complement renames or tells something about the subject.
>   EXAMPLES: Dogs are **animals** of the canine family. [noun]
>   Anna seems **friendly** to you but not to me. [adjective]
>   The person behind the mask was **you**. [pronoun]
> - Understanding subject complements will help you to choose the correct pronoun case (see Lesson 37).

**A. Circle the noun, pronoun, or adjective that functions as the subject complement, and underline any words that modify it.**

1. This car is faster than mine.

2. Your face appears quite flushed.

3. I feel a terrible pain in my side.

4. Hans remained completely silent.

5. The biggest challenge for our health-care system is long waiting lists for services.

6. Julie's plans for college sound very ambitious.

7. This is a photo of me on holiday in France.

8. Your calculation of the tax seems unusually high.

9. Winning the marathon would be a dream come true.

10. That pot of soup tastes hearty, healthy, and delicious!

> - When a pronoun is the subject complement, it is correct to use the subjective case (I, you, she, he, it, we, they, who), not the objective case (me, you, her, him, it, us, them, whom).
>   EXAMPLE: **Incorrect:** The best speaker in the class was her.
>   **Correct:** The best speaker in the class was she.
> - If the construction sounds awkward, try rephrasing or reversing the sentence.
>   EXAMPLE: She was the best speaker in the class.

**B. For each sentence, choose the correct pronoun given in parentheses. If the sentence sounds awkward, rewrite it on the line.**

1. The best actor in the play was (he, him). _____

2. The police will help (we, us). _____

3. The culprit had to be (she, her). _____

4. The only loser in this situation might be (I, me). _____

5. The guy in the limousine almost hit (I, me). _____

- We have already seen that sentences can be divided into subjects and predicates. Another way to analyse the parts of a sentence is to look at the clauses and phrases within the sentence.

- A **clause** is a group of words that contains both a subject and a predicate. Every complete sentence has at least one clause, and some have several (see Lesson 20).

  EXAMPLES: Theo relaxed. [one clause]
  John sang  while Margot played guitar. [two clauses]
  Jan knocked  when she arrived but nobody answered.
  [three clauses]

- A clause often contains several phrases. A **phrase** is a group of closely related words that function together as a single part of speech, such as a noun, verb, adjective, or adverb. The example below is a single clause that contains four different kinds of phrases.

  noun phrase       verb phrase    adv. phrase   adj. phrase (modifies "street")

  EXAMPLE:  My Uncle Fred has always lived on the street opposite the park.

- Note that phrases are sometimes called after the type of words that form them. For example, adjective and adverb phrases that begin with a preposition (in, of, through, with, etc.) are often called prepositional phrases. You will learn more about these and other specific kinds of noun, adjective, and adverb phrases in Lessons 31 and 43.

- Knowing the difference between a phrase and a clause will help you to write complete sentences and avoid unintentional sentence fragments (see Lesson 21). The ability to write in complete sentences is a sign that the writer's ideas are well thought out.

**Indicate whether the underlined groups of words make a phrase (P) or a clause (C). Write your answer in the space above each line.**

William Shakespeare is considered by many to be the greatest writer in the English language. His works are still read and enjoyed by millions, and his insight into human nature holds as true today as it did four hundred years ago. But little is known about Shakespeare himself. His life, beyond the bare facts of where he lived, whom he married, and when he was born and died, is a mystery.

We do not even know what he looked like. Until recently, only two portraits of Shakespeare existed, and both are believed to have been painted after his death. Now, a portrait has turned up in Ontario that may be the only existing likeness of the bard painted during his lifetime. According to the owner of the work, the painting has been in his family for generations. In fact, it spent decades lying under a bed and up in an attic!

Tests on the wood show that it is about 400 years old, and the paint is about the same age. This dates it at about the time when Shakespeare was alive. X-rays have also confirmed that the portrait is not painted over another, older painting.

So, is it Shakespeare? We may never know for sure. The owner of the painting is conducting a search into his family history to look for more clues. In the meantime, the painting is on display at the Art Gallery of Ontario in Toronto. Many people have looked for clues to Shakespeare's personality in the picture. They note the bright, intelligent eyes and mischievous expression, and imagine these features may be able to fill in some of those blanks in our understanding of Shakespeare, the man.

# Lesson 15

## Independent and Subordinate Clauses

- Two types of clauses are used in sentences. An **independent clause** can stand alone as a sentence because it expresses a complete thought.

    EXAMPLES: Inigo sneezes.
    The cat hissed at my dog.

- A **subordinate clause** needs an independent clause to complete its meaning. Most subordinate clauses begin with a subordinating conjunction, such as when, as, if, because, since, or a relative pronoun, such as that, which, who, or whom. In the following example sentences, the independent clause is underlined once and the subordinate clause is underlined twice.

    EXAMPLES: Inigo sneezes when he is near pollen.
    The cat that is called Scarface hissed at my dog.

**A.** Underline the independent clause once and subordinate clauses (if any), twice.

1. Although the North and South Poles are extremely difficult regions to live in, many animals have found ways of adapting to the extreme conditions.

2. The Arctic tern lives in the Arctic during the summer, when the weather there is relatively warm.

3. Before winter weather arrives, it flies to the Antarctic to spend summer there.

4. Since the trip each way is over 20 000 kilometres, the tern is the most travelled bird on earth.

5. No large animals live year-round in the Antarctic, because it is too cold.

6. The largest permanent resident is a tiny insect called a midge, which cannot fly as other midges do, because it has no wings.

7. Even if the midges had wings, they would not be able to use them because it is too windy.

8. The ice fish, whose body is transparent, survives because its blood contains a kind of antifreeze.

9. Polar bears are perfectly adapted to the harsh conditions in the far north.

10. Their thick coat is made up of hollow hairs to trap the heat from the sun.

11. Anyone who lives in the Arctic respects the ferocious killing power of these predators.

- Sometimes, that, who, or whom may be omitted at the beginning of a subordinate clause if the meaning of the sentence is clear.

    EXAMPLE: The company [that] I worked for last summer was great.

**B.** Underline the subordinate clause(s) in each sentence.

1. The card I played last turn was the queen of diamonds.

2. This new chef they hired creates delicious new recipes all the time.

3. The music Cecilia's band performed at the festival sounded great.

4. A passenger I met on the train told me about a great place to stay.

# Lesson 16 — Adjective, Adverb, and Noun Clauses

- Subordinate clauses can act as adjectives, adverbs, or nouns in a sentence. Understanding the function of a clause will help you to build well-constructed sentences and avoid misplaced modifiers (see Lesson 45).
- An **adjective clause** is a subordinate clause that modifies a noun or a pronoun. It answers the adjective questions <u>which one</u> or <u>what kind</u> about the noun or pronoun that comes before it. Most adjective clauses begin with a relative pronoun, such as <u>who</u>, <u>whom</u>, <u>whose</u>, <u>that</u>, or <u>which</u>.
  EXAMPLE: People **who exercise regularly** are less likely to get sick.

**A. Underline the adjective clause in each of the following sentences, and then circle the noun or pronoun it modifies.**

1. The crossword puzzles that Nicholas likes to do are published in *The Herald*.

2. This new legislation is good news for anyone who is interested in protecting the environment.

3. This car, which I bought for next to nothing, has proved to be incredibly reliable.

4. The fellow whose dog I found called to thank me.

5. The commander, whom we all liked and respected, was reassigned to another division.

- An **adverb clause** is a subordinate clause that modifies a verb, an adjective, or another adverb. It answers the adverb questions <u>how</u>, <u>under what conditions</u>, or <u>why</u>. Adverb clauses usually begin with a subordinating conjunction, such as <u>when</u>, <u>after</u>, <u>before</u>, <u>since</u>, <u>although</u>, or <u>because</u>.
  EXAMPLES: **Although she was nominated in three categories**, she did not win a Gemini.
  I went to Queen's **because it has a good Law program**.

**B. Underline the adverb clause in the following sentences. Circle the verb it modifies.**

1. You could visit us in Paris if you can get time off.

2. Although we won 6-3, it was a close game until late in the third period.

3. I'll join you once I catch my breath.

4. Call whenever you can.

5. Until we speak to Barbara directly, we won't know what happened.

**C. Underline the subordinate clause in each of the following sentences. Identify each clause as an adjective clause (ADJ) or an adverb clause (ADV).**

1. I'll give Marta a lift, since I'm going in that direction. _____

2. The time limit that the instructor gave us for completing this test is unreasonable. _____

3. We only got tickets because Casey knows someone in the band. _____

4. The herb echinacea helps fight colds, especially those that begin with a sore throat. _____

5. Whether we want to or not, we have to shovel that snow. _____

> ■ A **noun clause** is a subordinate clause that acts as a noun in a sentence. Most noun clauses answer the questions <u>who</u> or <u>what</u>. Noun clauses are often introduced by words like <u>when</u>, <u>what</u>, <u>that</u>, <u>whatever</u>, <u>whoever</u>, <u>whomever</u>, <u>whenever</u>, or <u>however</u>.
>
> EXAMPLES: <u>Whoever washed the dishes</u> did a good job. (*Who* did a good job?)
>
> Amir always knows exactly <u>what I am thinking</u>. (Amir knows *what*?)
>
> The best part of the movie was <u>when Jackie Chan jumped off the moving train</u>. (*When* was the best part?)
>
> Do your best with <u>what you've got</u>. (Do your best with *what*?)

**D. Underline the noun clause in each of the following sentences.**

1. However you want to arrange the furniture is fine with me.

2. I'm starting to understand what you mean.

3. Kayla has always done whatever she wants.

4. The restaurant is not far from where I live.

5. Jackie knows how we can beat the traffic.

**E. Underline each subordinate clause and label it <u>ADJ</u> for adjective, <u>ADV</u> for adverb, or <u>N</u> for noun.**

1. In 1954, the Canadian National Exhibition (CNE) offered $10 000 to Florence Chadwick if she could swim Lake Ontario.

2. Chadwick was a well-known American swimmer who had recently crossed the English Channel.

3. The CNE hoped that the swim would generate publicity for the Exhibition.

4. Chadwick did not know at first that two other swimmers were also planning to swim the lake.

5. One of these challengers was Winnie Roach, who had been the first Canadian to swim the Channel.

6. The other was an unknown 16-year-old Toronto schoolgirl, whose name was Marilyn Bell.

7. Since the CNE was backing Chadwick, they did not offer any money to the other two swimmers.

8. As all three swimmers entered the water at Youngstown, New York, on the evening of September 8, 1954, the eyes of the country were upon them.

9. When the next day dawned, both Chadwick and Roach had already given up.

10. Even though she was dazed and disoriented, Bell stayed in the water, facing four-metre-high waves, chilly water, and strong winds.

11. Lamprey eels, which kept attaching themselves to her legs, often distracted her.

12. Because of the wind blowing her off course, Bell's coach later estimated that she swam about 100 kilometres in total, twice the actual distance from Youngstown to Toronto.

13. At about 8:15 p.m. on September 9th, almost twenty-one hours after she entered the lake, Marilyn Bell touched a breakwater on the Toronto shoreline near the CNE grounds.

14. Thousands of people who had been following her progress on the radio met her at the pier.

15. What she had accomplished was enough to convince the CNE to give her the $10 000 originally offered to Florence Chadwick.

## Sentence Structure

- There are four basic types of sentence structure, each composed of various combinations of independent and subordinate clauses, as the chart that follows shows.
- Using a variety of different sentence types helps to make your writing more interesting. For more on Sentence Variety, see Lesson 20.

| Sentence Type | Composed of | Examples |
|---|---|---|
| Simple | one **independent clause** | **Darren travelled to Spain.** |
| Compound | two or more **independent clauses** joined by a semi-colon or a co-ordinating conjunction (and, or, nor, for, but, so, yet) | **Darren travelled to Spain;** **I stayed home.**<br><br>**Darren travelled to Spain** but **I stayed home.** |
| Complex | one **independent clause** and one or more subordinate clauses | **Darren travelled to Spain** when he was twenty. |
| Compound–Complex | two or more **independent clauses** and one or more subordinate clauses (in other words, a compound sentence with at least one subordinate clause added) | **Darren travelled to Spain** when he was twenty, but **I stayed home.** |

**Label each of the following sentences as simple (S), compound (CP), complex (CX), or compound–complex (CC). Remember that a simple sentence can have a compound subject or predicate.**

1. John dropped his favourite tuque. _____

2. Take this letter to the bank and ask them to explain what it means. _____

3. Elena watched the game but she didn't enjoy it. _____

4. I have never been to a monster truck rally, nor do I ever intend to go to one. _____

5. Every Saturday, Hayden and I walk to the market and buy vegetables. _____

6. For the whole week, students had to care for a doll as if it were a real baby. _____

7. All of the contestants tried and failed to answer the question. _____

8. Montréal's reputation as a cosmopolitan city is well deserved, although Toronto is more

   multicultural. _____

9. It's raining, so take an umbrella if you go out. _____

10. Hyung makes delicious pizza, but whenever I try making it, it tastes awful! _____

# Lesson 18

## Co-ordination and Subordination

- Two elements of a sentence are **co-ordinate** if they have equal value or weight. Express ideas of equal importance by joining them with a co-ordinating conjunction (and, or, nor, for, but, so, yet), or by linking them with a semicolon, as in a compound sentence.

    EXAMPLE:  James has published six books, and the seventh is coming out next month. [both statements have equal importance]

- Less important, or **subordinate** ideas, should be joined to main ideas as phrases or as subordinate clauses. In complex sentences with one subordinate and one independent clause, be sure to put the idea that you feel is most important in the independent clause.

    EXAMPLES: Although I never win, I buy lottery tickets every week. [the most important idea is that the lottery tickets are bought every week]
    Although I buy lottery tickets every week, I never win. [the most important idea is never winning]

- Remember that subordinating clauses and phrases cannot stand alone as a sentence without an independent clause (see Lessons 15 and 21).

**A.  Use proofreader's marks to combine the following sentences so that the first idea is subordinate.**

1. Charles Dickens came from an impoverished family. He writes with great compassion about the poor.

2. I just combed my hair. It looks messy.

3. Do something worthwhile with your life. Happiness will follow.

4. I try to raise my arm. Then, I get a sharp pain in my shoulder blade.

5. You need to get a referral from your doctor. Until then, the specialist will not see you.

- Avoid the common tendency to join clauses with and when another conjunction more accurately expresses the relationship.

    EXAMPLE: **Faulty Co-ordination:**  We agreed to meet on Tuesday, and you never showed up.
    **Better (co-ordinated):**  We agreed to meet on Tuesday, but you never showed up.
    **Better (subordinated):** Although we agreed to meet on Tuesday, you never showed up.

**B.  Revise the following sentences in your notebook, replacing and with a more appropriate conjuction.**

1. Annie's dad must have been very proud of her, and he bragged about her to his friends.

2. Our expenses are too high and we have to reduce spending.

3. Journalists try to stick to the facts, and they don't always succeed.

4. By the end of Act 2, the main character has developed more self-confidence, and this change becomes clear when she decides to leave her job.

5. Alcohol impairs your judgment, and it is easy to believe that you are more sober than you really are.

# Lesson 19

Words, phrases, and clauses that act as adjectives can be restrictive or non-restrictive.

- **Restrictive elements** contain information that is necessary to the meaning of the sentence. Restrictive elements should never be set off from the rest of the sentence by punctuation.

    EXAMPLES: The room filled with flowers looked beautiful.

    That singer who won a Juno last year has another hit album.

- **Non-restrictive elements** are descriptive, but not essential to the meaning of the sentence. No necessary information is lost if they are removed. Non-restrictive elements are set off from the rest of the sentence by commas, dashes, or parentheses. In the examples below, notice how the meaning of the sentence is altered when a phrase or clause is changed from restrictive to non-restrictive.

    EXAMPLES: The room, filled with flowers, looked beautiful.

    That singer, who won a Juno last year, has another hit album.

**Identify each underlined phrase or clause as either restrictive (R) or non-restrictive (NR). Add missing punctuation where it is needed.**

1. _____ Marketers who seem willing to go to any lengths to persuade us to buy their products have found a new way to probe our minds.

2. _____ The Brighthouse Institute for Thought Sciences a company based in Atlanta, Georgia, is using MRI technology to scan the brains of consumers.

3. _____ Advertisers hope that the MRIs will reveal our true feelings about ads or products they are trying to sell.

4. _____ Subjects who are paid for their participation are shown pictures of products while they are lying inside an MRI machine.

5. _____ The technology has attracted the attention of many companies looking for a marketing edge.

6. _____ Ninety-five percent of all our thoughts and emotions occur at the subconscious level, in parts of the brain unreachable by marketers—until now.

7. _____ By presenting images to subjects and then scanning their brains, researchers are hoping they can create advertisements which are emotionally compelling.

8. _____ But some observers are skeptical about how effective this new technique which has been dubbed "neuromarketing" will be.

9. _____ After all, consumers today especially teenagers and young adults are very sophisticated in their understanding of how media works.

10. _____ Consumers are fully aware of the techniques marketers use to persuade them, so perhaps they are less easily manipulated by these tricks.

# Lesson 20

## Sentence Variety

- To make your writing interesting, try to use a variety of sentence types and lengths. Avoid using too many sentences with the same pattern, length, or structure in a row, unless you are doing so intentionally to create a specific effect (for example, to emphasize a point or to create suspense).

  EXAMPLES: **Original:** Long-distance running is a tough sport. It requires exceptional endurance. Marathon runners have to train hard.

  **Revised:** Long-distance running is a tough sport; it requires exceptional endurance, so marathon runners have to train hard.

  **Revised:** Long-distance running is a tough sport that requires exceptional endurance, so marathon runners have to train hard.

  **Revised:** Because long-distance running is a tough sport that requires exceptional endurance, marathon runners have to train hard.

**A.** **Revise the following paragraphs to create a variety of sentence structures and lengths. Use proofreader's marks to make the changes. Sentences in square brackets can stay as they are. Your final revision should include all four kinds of sentences: simple, compound, complex, and compound–complex.**

**(1)** Tom Longboat was once Canada's greatest long-distance runner. His achievements have often been overlooked. [He was born on the Six Nations Reserve near Brantford, Ontario, in 1887.] **(2)** His father died in 1903. His mother was left to raise four children on her own. The family was very poor.

**(3)** Even as a child, Longboat loved to run. He trained on the reserve under another great runner, Bill Davis. **(4)** Longboat entered the Around-the-Bay Race in Hamilton in 1906. He was 19. **(5)** Most spectators had never heard of him. They were not very impressed with how he looked, either. **(6)** He stood at the starting line. People laughed. He was wearing cheap running shoes and a swimsuit in place of shorts. **(7)** Then he started running. Suddenly, his appearance did not seem important. [Longboat won the race easily. In fact, he came close to setting a new record for the course.]

**(8)** In 1907, Longboat won the Boston Marathon. Once again he broke the existing record. **(9)** No one beat his time until years later. The course was made easier then.

[Longboat now set his sights on running in the 1908 Olympics.] **(10)** Everyone expected him to win. It was not to be. **(11)** The runners headed into the last few kilometres. Longboat was in second place. He was renowned for finishing strongly. **(12)** The crowd was waiting for him to make his move. Longboat suddenly collapsed on the track. [People were stunned.] **(13)** Some thought that he had been drugged. No evidence to support this theory was ever found, however. [Longboat recovered and soon resumed his running career.]

- In addition to using sentences of different lengths and structure, you can add variety to your writing by using a mixture of loose and periodic sentences.
- A **loose sentence** begins with the main subject and the main verb; modifying phrases and clauses are added at the end.

  EXAMPLE: **The rowers** *waited* with tensed muscles, sweat-stained brows, and looks of grim determination.
- A **periodic sentence** puts off the main idea until the end. This arrangement, when used in moderation, can be a very effective way to draw a reader along and add emphasis to the main idea.

  EXAMPLE: With tensed muscles, sweat-stained brows, and looks of grim determination, **the rowers** *waited*.

**B. Improve the flow of the following passage by changing four of the six periodic sentences to loose sentences. Write your changes in the space above each line.**

In order to enlist in the army during the First World War, Longboat chose to set aside his promising professional running career. Carrying documents and messages from one military post to another, he served as a messenger with the 107th Pioneer Battalion. Twice while in France, Longboat was wounded. At one point, due to some bureaucratic error, he was declared dead. When he returned home in 1919, after four long years of war, his wife had remarried. Since no one had bothered to inform her of the mistake, she had assumed she was a widow.

- Most sentences are written in **natural order**, with the subject before the verb. Sentences in which the verb comes before the subject are in **inverted order**.

  EXAMPLES: **Natural Order: A vine** <u>climbed</u> along the side of the shed.
  **Inverted Order:** Along the side of the shed <u>climbed</u> **a vine**.
- Adding the occasional sentence that does not follow natural order is another way to keep your writing interesting. Use inverted-order sentences sparingly, however, or your writing may sound overly formal.

**C. Find three examples of sentences in inverted order in the following paragraphs. Use proofreader's marks to change these sentences to natural order. In your notebook, describe how the tone of the passage was affected by the use of inverted order. Explain which version you prefer, and why.**

Tom Longboat's fortunes declined after the War. Gone were the glory days of his early career. Forgotten were his moments of triumph at the Boston Marathon. He worked as a garbage collector for the City of Toronto for twenty years, and died in 1949.

Longboat endured a lot of racism during his career. But never once did he complain about it. Today, several long-distance races are named after him, and a stamp was commissioned to commemorate his contribution to Canadian sport.

# Lesson 21

## Sentence Fragments

> ■ A **sentence fragment** is formed when a group of words that is not a complete sentence—such as a subordinate clause, a phrase, or a single word—is nevertheless punctuated as a complete sentence.
>
> EXAMPLES: **Fragment:** I would save that letter. <u>Because you may need it.</u>
> **Revised:** I would save that letter. You may need it. **OR**
> I would save that letter, because you may need it.
>
> **Fragment:** No one will do that job. <u>Not for such low pay</u>.
> **Revised:** No one will do that job for such low pay.
>
> **Fragment:** I can't come to your house. <u>Unfortunately</u>.
> **Revised:** Unfortunately, I can't come to your house.
>
> ■ Fragments are acceptable in some situations (for example, when writing dialogue, in advertising slogans, to create a very informal tone, or sometimes as an answer to a question). However, unintentional sentence fragments should be avoided. They may make your reader think you have not thought through your ideas thoroughly.
>
> ■ Remember that commands have an implied subject, so they are not fragments.
> EXAMPLES: Stop!     Come here.     Help!     Don't cry.

**A. Identify each sentence below as either a complete sentence (S) or a fragment (F).**

1. It's your life. _____ Make something of it. _____

2. Mercury-brand running shoes. _____ Simply the best. _____

3. Carl is a trusting guy. _____ Trusting, yes, but not naive. _____

4. We had a great time at the farm, doing whatever we pleased. _____ Riding horses, hiking through the woods, swimming in the lake. _____

5. Wait! _____ There's a tree across the path. _____

**B. Use proofreader's marks to eliminate the fragments in the following paragraph.**

Humans dressed up as birds, puppets, and ultralight planes. These are the ingredients in an ambitious plan to save the endangered whooping crane population of North America. And it's working. Slowly. Back in 1940, the entire whooping crane population was estimated at less than twenty. Now, the captive and wild population has increased to about 400. Not bad, given the obstacles that had to be overcome. Whooping crane chicks are being raised in captivity, by handlers dressed in white to hide their human form, with crane-head puppets attached to their arms. Which they use to teach the young birds crane behaviour. When it is time to migrate south, the young cranes do not have adult cranes to lead them, so they don't know the way. That's where the ultralights come in. The handlers teach the chicks to follow the ultralight. All the way south to their safe winter habitat in Florida.

# Run-on Sentences and Comma-Splice Errors

- A **run-on sentence** has too many clauses joined without a co-ordinating conjunction (and, or, nor, for, but, so, or yet) or proper punctuation. To avoid run-ons, remember that independent clauses must be joined by a semicolon or a co-ordinating conjunction, or both. Words such as therefore, however, and nevertheless cannot join two clauses without a semicolon or a period.

  EXAMPLE: **Run-on:** The sky was overcast nevertheless, the race went ahead.
  **Correct:** The sky was overcast; nevertheless, the race went ahead.
  The sky was overcast. Nevertheless, the race went ahead.
  Although the sky was overcast, the race went ahead.
  The sky was overcast, but the race went ahead.

- When two independent clauses are joined by only a comma and no conjunction, the result is a **comma-splice error**.

  EXAMPLE: **Comma-Splice Error:** Get dressed, we have to go.
  **Correct:** Get dressed; we have to go.
  Get dressed. We have to go.
  Get dressed, because we have to go.
  Get dressed, for we have to go.

**Correct any run-on sentences or comma-splice errors using proofreader's marks. If the sentences are joined correctly, label them C.**

1. The poem begins with a series of beautiful images of nature then it slowly reveals the cruelty that lies beneath.

2. Every morning, I buy a cup of coffee and a muffin at the drive-through, it's become a ritual that I can't do without.

3. If conditions are good, cornstalks get tall very quickly; some farmers even swear you can hear the stalks growing, but I don't believe it.

4. Stop worrying start planning.

5. You should go see that film, it's terrific.

6. I was really excited about my new portable CD player however, it doesn't work.

7. Don't be afraid to speak up about what you think is important, so people know what you stand for.

8. No one really knows what causes those mysterious crop circles, I doubt the solution involves aliens though, as some people have suggested.

9. Ry Cooder is not just a great musician he's a musicologist.

10. This politician's record speaks for itself she has always stood up for those in need.

11. I hate it when you leave your towel in a heap on the bathroom floor for me to pick up it's not fair.

12. Whatever you think of John's paintings, you have to admit he is talented.

13. Take your medicine it's good for you.

14. Traffic is more congested in the city centre in addition, parking can be very expensive.

15. I don't know what you mean by that statement, neither does Ms. Mah.

 **Unit 2, Sentences**

**A.** **In each sentence below, underline the words that are identified in parentheses.**

   **1.** (simple subject) There is a message for you on the answering machine.

   **2.** (simple predicate) In the past fifty years, computer technology has changed the world.

   **3.** (compound subject) Will Carla and her friends stay at a hotel or a bed and breakfast?

   **4.** (complete predicate) Larissa will be representing the school at a track meet in Halifax.

   **5.** (direct object) Mackenzie's brother brought her some interesting gifts from Turkey.

   **6.** (indirect object) Dr. Lindstrom gave the nurse on duty some instructions regarding the patient.

   **7.** (subject complement) The next person to get hurt may be you or someone you know.

   **8.** (complete subject) Working to improve the lives of people with cancer is the agency's main goal.

   **9.** (compound subject) Thinking quickly and knowing what to do in an emergency are two important skills for a paramedic.

   **10.** (subordinate clause) The book you ordered is out of print.


**B.** **Underline independent clauses once and subordinate clauses twice. Then, label each sentence as simple (S), compound (CP), complex (CX), or compound–complex (CC).**

   **1.** Canada's population is aging, and as many older workers retire, analysts are predicting a shortage of skilled tradespeople. _____

   **2.** People in some trades, such as electricians, plumbers, and tool and die makers, make a very good living, and experienced workers are almost guaranteed a job. _____

   **3.** Apprenticeship programs offer a great way to earn while you learn. _____

   **4.** You may start at the bottom doing chores, but over time the work, and your pay, will improve. _____

   **5.** Have you ever thought about learning a trade? _____


**C.** **Identify each word group as a phrase (P) or a clause (C).**

   **1.** withered and died _____

   **2.** whenever the wind blows from the east _____

   **3.** take your time _____

   **4.** in a small town on the border _____

   **5.** juggling oranges while riding a bike _____

   **6.** because Valentine's Day is next week _____

   **7.** expecting to do well without studying _____

   **8.** over there, on the top of the hill _____

   **9.** I guess so _____

   **10.** a parcel of land known as a seigneury _____

**D. Write sentences to match the descriptions given below.**

1. A sentence with an adjective clause _____

2. A sentence with an adverb clause _____

3. A sentence with a restrictive clause _____

4. A sentence with a non-restrictive clause _____

**E. Revise the following sentences, replacing <u>and</u> with a more appropriate co-ordinating or subordinating conjunction and making any other necessary changes. Use proofreader's marks.**

1. Jason spoke quietly at first and by the end of his speech he was practically yelling.

2. Giraffes have long necks, and they can feed off the highest branches of trees.

3. Gold prices are going up, and this is a sign that the economy is slowing down.

**F. Identify the following sentences as loose (L) or periodic (P).**

1. If wishes were horses, beggars would ride. _____

2. Working for hours with canvas, brushes, and paints, Dawna created her masterpiece. _____

3. The students filed in, some laughing and chatting, others looking grimly determined. _____

**G. Write each of the following inverted-order sentences in natural order.**

1. Hard on the heels of the first came a second volley of insults.

   _____

2. It is unfair to expect perfection from students or anyone else.

   _____

3. So loudly does he snore that no one in the house can get any sleep.

   _____

**H. Revise the following sentences using proofreader's marks to eliminate sentence fragments, run-on sentences, and comma-splice errors. Feel free to add words as needed.**

1. Deliver this letter to Ms. Jonas by hand, it contains important information.

2. While you are waiting in the lobby.

3. Take care, don't fall.

4. We don't usually accept returns however we will make an exception in your case.

5. The greatest show on earth, according to some.

6. *The Life of Pi*, a book by Canadian author Yann Martel, about a boy who finds himself stranded on a raft with a tiger.

7. The story kept my interest nevertheless it was the characters that really intrigued me.

# Using What You've Learned

**A.** **Read the following passage; then, answer the questions that follow.**

Is there something that you are supposed to be doing, but you just can't face it? ____ If so, join the club.

____ Most of us are guilty of procrastination at some time or another, but for some of us, avoiding

important tasks is a serious problem that needs to be addressed. ____ According to one psychologist,

about 20 to 25 percent of students are chronic procrastinators. ____ These students are often at risk of

dropping out of college or university. ____ But most of them are not lazy; they often work very, very hard

at avoiding the task at hand. ____ In the meantime, they may accomplish a great deal: cleaning out

drawers, organizing their pencils in a neat row, tidying up their desktop. ____

So, why do people procrastinate? ____ In some cases, they put off things because they are

perfectionists. ____ This may sound like a contradiction, but if you think about it, perhaps it's not. ____

Perfectionists think that it is not worth doing something if they cannot do it perfectly. ____ Therefore, when

a task seems overwhelming, they prefer to avoid it altogether. ____

If you are one of these people, the cure may be to break down each task into smaller pieces. ____

Don't focus on how difficult it will be to write a ten-page term paper; instead, think about the components

of the process. ____ Set a schedule, so you can allot yourself manageable chunks of work each day. ____

For example, on Day 1, your task might be to find five books that contain useful information. ____ That's all.

If you do one thing every day toward your goal, you will eventually reach it, without really noticing how you

got there. ____

**1.** Label each sentence in the above passage simple (S), compound (CP), complex (CX), or compound–complex (CC).

**2.** Find two sentences in the passage that are in inverted order and write them below.

_____

_____

_____

**3.** Find a sentence in the second paragraph that contains two subordinate clauses and write it on the lines below. Underline the noun clause once and the adverb clause twice.

_____

_____

**B. Rewrite the sentences below, using the sentence structure indicated in parentheses.**

1. If you are one of these people, the cure may be to break down each task into smaller pieces. (simple)

   _____

2. Set a schedule, so you can allot yourself manageable chunks of work each day. (complex)

   _____

3. According to one psychologist, about 20 to 25 percent of students are chronic procrastinators. These students are often at risk of dropping out of college or university. (compound–complex)

   _____

**C. Improve the passage that follows by implementing the changes that follow. Use proofreader's marks.**

- **eliminate two sentence fragments**
- **eliminate two run-on sentences**
- **eliminate two comma-splice errors**
- **change two uses of <u>and</u> to more appropriate conjunctions**
- **find two non-restrictive phrases that are not set off by commas, and add the necessary punctuation**
- **change one expletive construction to a natural-order sentence**

In 1613, the explorer and geographer Samuel de Champlain visited Canada. For the third and last time, travelling along the Ottawa River to take measurements and draw maps. Somewhere along the way, during a portage, Champlain lost his astrolabe. In the 1600s, an astrolabe was an important instrument for measuring distance it worked like a primitive version of today's Global Positioning Systems. Champlain never recovered it, and the instrument remained lost for over two centuries.

In 1867, Edward Lee a fourteen-year-old boy was working with his father in a wooded area near Green Lake, Ontario. He came across a strange-looking instrument, it turned out to be an astrolabe. A riverboat captain offered to buy the instrument from Lee for ten dollars. Lee accepted the offer and he never saw the money. The astrolabe was eventually sold to a collector in New York and finally willed to the New York Historical Society, in 1989, the Canadian Museum of Civilization in Ottawa bought the artifact.

Is this Champlain's lost astrolabe? There is some evidence suggesting that it may be. For one thing, the date on the instrument which is 1603 may be significant. It corresponds to the date when Champlain received his commission from the King of France, and perhaps the astrolabe was given to Champlain to commemorate that occasion. Also, the instrument's readings are out by one degree, and so were the readings Champlain recorded before losing the instrument.

In any case, the astrolabe is now on display in Ottawa, at the Museum of Civilization. Where you can visit and draw your own conclusions. While you are there, you may want to visit the statue of Champlain on Sussex Drive. The statue shows Champlain holding up his astrolabe against the sky, as if taking a reading. But the sculptor made a mistake the astrolabe is upside down!

A **noun** is a word that names a person, place, thing, or idea. The three main classes of nouns are as follows:

- A **common noun** names a person, place, thing, or idea in general.
    EXAMPLES: doctor, building, trophy
- A **proper noun** names a specific person, place, or thing. Proper nouns always begin with a capital letter.
    EXAMPLES: Doctor Kumarsamy, City Hall, Stanley Cup
- A **collective noun** is a noun that names a whole class or group of objects or people.
    EXAMPLES: jury, committee, herd

**A.** Find one example of each class of nouns in each sentence that follows. Underline common nouns once and proper nouns twice. Circle collective nouns.

1. Most actors who win an Oscar like to thank everyone from their accountant to their support group!

2. The committee responsible for testing athletes at the Olympics to make sure they are not using drugs tries to be fair to all participants.

3. All three traditional political parties have produced great leaders, among them Tommy Douglas, Pierre Trudeau, and Sir John A. Macdonald.

4. We can beat the team from St. Michael's School with our eyes closed!

5. When the band played "Satisfaction" by the Rolling Stones, the crowd went wild.

6. Begg, Barreau, and Steele is an accounting firm with a solid reputation.

7. My book club is reading a novel called *Fugitive Pieces* by Anne Michaels.

8. My family and I have visited many great monuments, from the Eiffel Tower to the Wawa Goose!

9. Scientists hope that Flipper, the young beluga, will rejoin his pod.

10. The administration is planning to increase tuition for students entering the Faculty of Medicine.

11. "There's a herd of angry buffalo coming this way!" yelled Wanda.

12. Along the shore of Rockwood Lake, I saw a school of minnows dart by.

13. That whole block of houses is scheduled to be demolished to make room for a McDonald's.

14. The staff at that camp is planning a trip to Algonquin Park next week.

15. In Scotland, each clan has its own tartan.

- A noun may function as a subject (S), direct object (DO), indirect object (IO), or subject complement (SC) in a sentence.
    EXAMPLE:       S                    SC                        IO        DO
        Dr. Samuels is the veterinarian who gives our dog its shots.
- When a noun follows a preposition, such as in, of, with, through, by, and between, it usually functions as the **object of the preposition**.
    EXAMPLE: Without **doubt**, an earthquake of that **magnitude** would knock dishes from the **cupboards** and leave cracks in the **sidewalk**.

**B. Underline the nouns in the following sentences. Then, identify each noun as a subject (S), direct object (DO), indirect object (IO), subject complement (SC), or object of a preposition (OP).**

1. You can download the latest version of that software from the Web.

2. Send Rocky a postcard when you get to Katmandu.

3. The manager of the department lost the stylus for her handheld computer.

4. The courier should arrive to pick up the package before five.

5. This trip is a disaster!

6. All these loonies and toonies are a strain on my pockets.

7. When Bob offers you a game of chess, beware!

8. A huge pile of butter in the shape of a dove sat in the middle of the table.

9. Nazrin sent her family an e-mail about her amazing discovery.

10. My cat, Herbie, likes to pretend that he is a dog.

11. Games that rely on luck are less of a challenge than those that involve skill.

12. Both parties are in agreement about the settlement.

13. The box at the back of the cupboard in the study contains my will.

14. Sayan wrote the manager a letter that explained her sudden departure.

15. Give the children some soup for their supper, please.

---

- Using precise nouns can help make your writing more engaging.
  - EXAMPLE: **Weak:** Thoughts of food distracted her from her writing.
  - **Stronger:** Visions of roast chicken, spaghetti, and ice cream sundaes distracted her from her writing.

---

**C. Rewrite the following passage, changing the vague expressions that are underlined for more precise words or phrases. Use a thesaurus or dictionary to help you find replacements, if necessary.**

I was walking through the local area on a warm summer evening. The sound of someone playing music on an instrument drifted down from an upper window. People were out on their front porches, fanning themselves, sipping drinks, and greeting people as they passed by. A group of kids was playing a game. Up above, a bird perched in a tree screamed her feeling about being disturbed.

_____

_____

_____

_____

_____

# Lesson 24

## Plural and Possessive Nouns

> ■ **Plural nouns** refer to more than one person, place, thing, or idea.

**A.** The following chart shows how to change singular nouns into plural nouns. Fill in the blanks in the third column with your own examples.

| Description | Plural Form | Examples |
|---|---|---|
| Most nouns | Add -s | card → card**s** |
| Nouns ending in a consonant + -y | Change the -y to -i and add -es | party → part**ies** |
| Nouns ending in -o | Add -s or -es | piano → piano**s** |
| | | potato → potato**es** |
| Nouns ending in -f or -fe | Add -s | belief → belief**s** |
| | Change the -f or -fe to -ve and add -s | life → li**ves** |
| | (**Note**: Some words have two plural forms.) | roof → roo**fs** or roo**ves** |
| | | _____ or _____ |
| Most nouns ending in -ch, -sh, -s, or -x | Add -es | bench → bench**es** |
| | | sash → sash**es** |
| | | kiss → kiss**es** |
| | | box → box**es** |
| Two- or three-word compound nouns | Generally, add -s to the most important word | jack-in-the-box → jack-in-the-**boxes** |
| | | governor-general → **governors**-general |
| Most nouns ending in -ful | Add -s to -ful | mouthful → mouth**fuls** |
| Nouns with irregular plural forms | Usually either<br>• change the middle vowel, | goose → g**ee**se |
| | • retain the same form as the singular, or | moose → m**oo**se |
| | • add -en | ox → ox**en** |

- Form the **possessive case** of most singular nouns by adding -'s.
  - EXAMPLES: the chicken's beak    one month's holiday
- Form the possessive of most regular plurals that end in -s by adding an apostrophe (') only.
  - EXAMPLES: the chickens' beaks    two months' holiday
- Form the possessive of most plural nouns that do not end in -s by adding -'s.
  - EXAMPLES: the women's book club
- Many people confuse plurals and possessives, adding apostrophes where none are necessary. Use the possessive form only if you can reword the phrase using <u>of</u> or <u>for</u>. Also remember that a possessive noun is always followed by another noun.
  - EXAMPLES: summer's end = the end of summer
    children's toys = toys for children
    two days' wait = a wait of two days

**B. Circle the correct possessive and/or plural word from the choices given in parentheses.**

1. The (cars, car's, cars') engine finally seized.

2. The (teachers, teacher's, teachers') decision was to let her (students, student's, students') leave early after the field trip.

3. Three (doctors, doctor's, doctors') examined the (patients, patient's, patients') broken leg.

4. That movie was the (critics, critic's, critics') choice at the Toronto Film Festival.

5. We ordered three (cappuccinos, cappuccino's, cappuccinos'), but you only brought two.

6. All the (actors, actor's, actors') names were listed in alphabetical order in the credits.

7. My (parents, parent's, parents') cabin is very secluded.

8. Brad likes to wear (mens, men's, mens') cologne.

- In some cases, it sounds awkward to use the possessive form with an inanimate object. Avoid awkward possessive forms in your writing by rewording them using a prepositional phrase.
  - EXAMPLE: **Awkward:** the apple's taste
    **Better:** the taste of the apple

**C. Rewrite the following passage in your notebook, eliminating errors in the use of possessives or plurals, and rewriting awkward possessive forms.**

One minute, Sinda was riding along the forest path on his way home. The next, he was on his face, sucking up mouthful's of leaf's and dirt. It took him a few minute's to realize what had happened. His bike had ridden over a tree stump that stood in the path's middle, hidden by some foliage's undergrowth. Sinda himself had gone flying, landing feet first at the ditch's bottom. He felt sore, especially his face and knee's, but nothing seemed to be broken. He examined his bike. The front wheel's rim was badly bent—he would have to walk the rest of the way, a good half-hours hike at least. It was getting dark already. Sinda shivered and fastened his jacket's buttons. Then, he stopped short. Two baby moose's were standing a few metres' away. And just behind them was the calfs mother, ready to protect her childrens' lives…. **[14 errors]**

> ■ A **verb** is a word or group of words that expresses an action or a state of being. Verbs can be one word or several words.
>   EXAMPLES: I <u>was</u> in the bath.     I <u>would have been</u> upset.

**A. Underline all the words that make up the verb in the following sentences.**

1. I speak three languages.

2. I would have made a great president.

3. I have not heard from Gabriel.

4. Several people are being honoured at the banquet.

5. In case of fire, pull the lever.

6. Before the event, three judges had been selected.

> ■ **Action verbs** express an action.
>   EXAMPLES: Josephine <u>walked</u> home.     I <u>was looking</u> for that ring!
>
> ■ **Linking verbs** describe a state of being. They link the subject to a word that describes or renames the subject. The most common linking verb is <u>be</u>.
>   EXAMPLES: Bai <u>is</u> in her room.     Lily <u>may be</u> our guest in March.
>   We <u>are</u> all fond of iced tea.     They <u>will be</u> on the plane by five.
>
> ■ Some verbs can act as either action verbs or linking verbs. If a verb can be replaced by a form of <u>be</u> in a sentence without significantly changing the meaning, it is acting as a linking verb.
>   EXAMPLES: **Action**                     **Linking**
>   The doctor <u>felt</u> my pulse.     I <u>felt</u> (or <u>was</u>) weak and dizzy.
>   Cassie <u>smelled</u> smoke.     The flowers <u>smell</u> (or <u>are</u>) lovely!
>   Daria <u>grew</u> vegetables.     Daria <u>grew</u> (or <u>was</u>) fond of her cat.
>
> ■ Understanding the difference between an action verb and a linking verb will help you to avoid mistakes in pronoun case (see Lesson 37). Choosing action verbs over linking verbs can also improve your writing.

**B. Underline the verbs in each of the following sentences. Write A if it is functioning as an action verb, or L if it is functioning as a linking verb.**

1. Elmira remained opposed to the plan, despite our cajoling. _____

2. Stephan remained behind to clean up after the party. _____

3. About three kilometres up the road, turn left at the lights. _____

4. The weather suddenly turned cold. _____

5. The instructions proved impossible to decipher. _____

6. The lawyer proved her case. _____

7. My hands got frostbitten. _____

8. I got six stitches for the cut on my knee. _____

9. That tiny, cute puppy will soon become a huge, scary dog! _____

## Principal Parts of Verbs

- The **principal parts** of a verb are the present, the past, the past participle, and the present participle. All other tenses and forms of the verb are formed from these principal parts.
- The **present** form of the verb is the form used in the first person, present tense.
- The **past** form of the verb is the form used in the first person, past tense.
- The **past participle** usually ends in -ed or -d. In regular verbs, the past and past participle are identical. To find the past participle, decide what form of the verb you would use after <u>have</u>.
- The **present participle** is formed by adding -ing to the infinitive (to talk, to handle, etc.).

EXAMPLES:

|  | Present | Past | Past Participle | Present Participle |
|---|---|---|---|---|
| **to talk** | (I) talk | (I) talked | (have) talked | talking |
| **to bake** | (I) bake | (I) baked | (have) baked | baking |

**A. Write the principal parts of the following regular verbs. Check a dictionary, if necessary.**

|  | Present | Past | Past Participle | Present Participle |
|---|---|---|---|---|
| **1.** to scream |  |  |  |  |
| **2.** to erase |  |  |  |  |
| **3.** to pull |  |  |  |  |
| **4.** to turn |  |  |  |  |
| **5.** to define |  |  |  |  |

- Many verbs do not follow the regular pattern for forming the principal parts. Often, the past and past-participle forms will differ. Dictionaries usually list irregular verb forms under the main entry for the verb.

EXAMPLES:

|  | Present | Past | Past Participle | Present Participle |
|---|---|---|---|---|
| **to hear** | hear | heard | (have) heard | hearing |
| **to fall** | fall | fell | (have) fallen | falling |

**B. Write the principal parts of the following irregular verbs. Check a dictionary, if necessary.**

|  | Present | Past | Past Participle | Present Participle |
|---|---|---|---|---|
| **1.** to cost |  |  |  |  |
| **2.** to fly |  |  |  |  |
| **3.** to choose |  |  |  |  |
| **4.** to rise |  |  |  |  |
| **5.** to know |  |  |  |  |

# Lesson 27

## Simple and Perfect Tenses

The **tense** of a verb indicates the time in which the action or state occurred.

- The **simple tenses** express actions or states occurring at an indefinite time in the past, present, or future.

  EXAMPLES: **Past**          **Present**          **Future**
  I played guitar.   I play guitar.   I will play guitar.

The **perfect tenses** allow you to indicate more precise time relationships.

- The **present perfect** (has or have + past participle) expresses an action or state that was completed (or perfected) at an indefinite time in the past, but still applies in the present. It can also express actions or states begun in the past and ongoing in the present.

  EXAMPLES: I have played guitar in this club once before. [completed in the past]
  Leo has played guitar for six years. [ongoing in the present]

- The past perfect (had + past participle) and **future perfect** (will have + past participle) express actions or states that were completed before some specific past time, or will be completed before a specific time in the future.

  EXAMPLES: **Past Perfect:** By age twelve, I had attended eight different schools.
  **Future Perfect:** As of June, I will have been in school for twelve years.

**A.** **The following sentences contain verbs in different tenses. Underline each verb in a simple tense once, and each verb in a perfect tense twice. Write the tense of each verb—past, present, or future—above each verb.**

1. I've had a lot of strange dreams in my life, but last night's was the strangest.

2. It has been a year since that star scored a box-office hit.

3. Until she met Joe, Carol had never understood what people mean by "love at first sight."

4. After I go through this garbage, I will have looked everywhere for my lost bracelet.

5. As he stepped into the rink, Tariq remembered the last time he had tried skating.

**B.** **Write the verbs in parentheses in the most appropriate perfect tense. Then, label each by writing PRP for present perfect, PP for past perfect, or FP for future perfect above the verb.**

1. When you introduce me to your sister, I (meet) _____ your whole family.

2. Armand (develop) _____ a reputation as a superb cook, and he maintains it by continually trying new and even more delicious recipes.

3. I'm sure that Darko (travel) _____ to every continent by the time he is twenty.

4. Pat (notice) _____ that Margo was looking downcast.

5. If you (catch) _____ my eye when you saw me on the train, I would have come by to say hello!

# Uses of the Present Tense

In addition to signifying a current action or state, the present tense is also used in the following ways:

- To express a future action or state
    - EXAMPLE:    I leave for college tomorrow.

- To express a general belief, scientific truth, or customary or repeated action
    - EXAMPLES:  Roxanne soon discovered that love is blind.
    - Sir Isaac Newton was the first to suggest that white light is composed of many different types of rays refracted at slightly different angles.
    - Every Wednesday after school we play rugby.

- To describe aspects of a literary work or film in essays or reviews
    - EXAMPLE:    E. Annie Proulx wrote the novel *The Shipping News*, which is set in a remote fishing village in Newfoundland.

**Underline 20 verbs in the following sentences that either COULD or SHOULD be changed to the present tense. Write the present-tense form of the verb in the space above each line.**

The bubonic plague ravaged Europe in the Middle Ages, reducing the continent's population by a third. Even today, about 3000 cases of plague were reported around the globe every year. The characteristic symptoms of bubonic plague included hugely swollen glands, fever, and spots that were red at first, and then turned black. Pneumonic plague, the more deadly of the two forms, attacked the lungs. While untreated plague victims had a high mortality rate, a course of modern antibiotics greatly reduced the risk of death.

The children's song "Ring Around a Rosie" was, according to some experts, a song about the plague. The "rosie" the song mentioned was probably a reference to the red sores that were signs of plague. In the Middle Ages, people did not know that germs caused disease. Many people in the fourteenth century believed that carrying a "posy" of herbs was a way to prevent infection, although we know now that such remedies were useless against such a strong bacterial infection.

The plague occurred regularly as a theme in many classic and modern literary works. Giovanni Boccaccio's fourteenth-century work the *Decameron* presented 100 stories told by a group of men and women who were in hiding in a villa outside Florence to escape the plague. Daniel Defoe's *A Journal of the Plague Year*, written in 1722, gave a very realistic, though fictional, account of life—and death—in London during the plague of 1664-65. And in 1947, French writer Albert Camus wrote *The Plague*, a novel about a doctor who voluntarily agreed to remain in a quarantine town during an outbreak of plague, risking his own life to help others. Camus' work explored the range of possible human responses to a universe that often seemed indifferent to human suffering.

# Lesson 29

## Progressive Tenses

> ■ **Progressive tenses** indicate a continuing action or state. All of the simple and perfect tenses have a progressive form. The progressive tense is formed by combining the verb <u>be</u> with the present participle.
>
> EXAMPLES: **Present Progressive:** Sara <u>is feeding</u> the pigeons in the park. The pigeons <u>are cooing</u> in appreciation.
>
> **Past Progressive:** The sun <u>was burning</u> my skin. The horses <u>were galloping</u> across the field.
>
> **Future Progressive:** The presentation <u>will be starting</u> soon.

**A.** Underline all the words that make up the verb in the progressive tense. Then, identify the progressive tense as present, past, or future.

1. I am glad that your cousins are meeting us. _____

2. I sneezed so hard I thought my head was coming off! _____

3. I will be calling four of you for an interview in the next few days. _____

4. The crowd was pushing us forward toward the stage. _____

5. Su-Mei is always looking for her glasses! _____

> ■ Use the **perfect progressive tenses** when you want to emphasize the ongoing nature of the action or state. Form the perfect progressive tenses as follows:
>
> EXAMPLES: **Present Perfect Progressive:** I <u>have been living</u> here all my life. He <u>has been living</u> here all his life.
>
> **Past Perfect Progressive:** We <u>had been waiting</u> for days.
>
> **Future Perfect Progressive:** Maddie <u>will have been working</u> for six hours by the time she finishes.

**B.** Underline all the words that make up the verbs in the perfect progressive tense. Identify the perfect progressive tense as past, present, or future.

1. I will have been waiting for six hours when Matteo finally arrives. _____

2. Taylor had been training for weeks in preparation for the marathon. _____

3. I have been thinking about what you told me the other day. _____

4. Hanif has been waiting patiently in line to buy tickets for all of us. _____

5. Just the day before, we had all been playing cards together, but now we were barely on

   speaking terms. _____

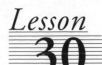

# Lesson 30

## Verbals: Participles, Gerunds, and Infinitives

> A **verbal** is a verb form that is not functioning as part of a verb. Three forms of verbals are participles, gerunds, and infinitives.
>
> ■ Participles can be used on their own as adjectives.
>
> > EXAMPLES: **Present Participle:** running feet     soothing music
> > **Past Participle:** printed page     fried eggs
>
> ■ The -ing form of a verb can also be used as a noun, in which case it is called a **gerund**. Like all nouns, gerunds can function as subjects or objects in a sentence.
>
> > EXAMPLES: Laughing with milk in your mouth is not advisable. [subject]
> > Patti watches wrestling every Saturday. [direct object]
> > You'll feel better just by smiling. [object of preposition]
> > Give your writing some flair! [indirect object]

**A. Underline the verbal in each sentence. Identify it as a participle (P) or a gerund (G).**

**1.** Sparring is the part I like best about karate. _____

**2.** One lost game is not the end of the world. _____

**3.** A skilled tradesperson could finish the job in half the time. _____

**4.** Have you considered teaching as a career? _____

**5.** If you like skateboarding, give inline skates a try. _____

**6.** I am looking for a folding chair for the balcony. _____

> ■ The **infinitive** is the basic form of the verb that is used after to. The infinitive can be used as a noun, an adjective, or an adverb.
>
> > EXAMPLES: To stay would be irresponsible. [noun]
> > My desire to sleep overcame my desire to eat. [adjectives]
> > The leaves are getting ready to fall. [adverb]

**B. Underline the infinitive in each sentence, and then identify its function as noun (N), adjective (ADJ), or adverb (ADV).**

**1.** Before we go down to the beach, I need a few minutes to unpack. _____

**2.** One way of winning at chess is to control the centre of the board. _____

**3.** To arrive late would be embarrassing. _____

**4.** Giving up is the surest way to fail. _____

**Unit 3, Grammar and Usage**

# Participial, Gerund, and Infinitive Phrases

> - A **participial phrase** consists of the present or past participle of a verb, along with any words that modify the participle. Participial phrases, like participles on their own, always act as adjectives in a sentence.
>
>    EXAMPLE:  <u>Holding on for dear life</u>, we tried not to scream as the roller coaster began its steep descent.
>
> - A **gerund phrase** consists of a gerund plus its modifiers. Like gerunds, gerund phrases always function as nouns.
>
>    EXAMPLES:  <u>Performing in front of a live audience</u> makes me nervous.
>    My little sister never tires of <u>climbing over the furniture</u>.
>    Pascal's hobby is <u>making paper airplanes</u>.
>    Most of us avoid <u>exercising at midday</u> when it is over 30°C.

**A.  Underline the participial or gerund phrases. Write <u>P</u> for participial phrase or <u>G</u> for gerund phrase.**

1. Conquering Niagara Falls has been an irresistible temptation for many people over the years. _____

2. One of the first people willing to attempt this feat was Annie Taylor. _____

3. In 1901, Taylor, wearing a long black dress and a hat, successfully plunged over the Horseshoe Falls in a barrel. _____

4. Maude Willard planned to shoot the rapids and the whirlpool beneath the Falls in a barrel made by another famous stunt performer, Carlisle Graham. _____

5. Graham had already used the barrel successfully, passing through the rapids and the whirlpool in 1886. _____

6. Willard added a twist by travelling with her pet dog. _____

7. Shooting the rapids was easy for Willard. _____

8. However, getting through the whirlpool proved more of a challenge. _____

9. Caught in the vortex of the whirlpool, the barrel spun round and round for six hours, its two inhabitants unable to escape. _____

10. When rescuers finally managed to retrieve the barrel and pry it open, they found the dog alive, and overjoyed to be released from his watery prison. _____

11. Willard, unfortunately, was dead, killed by suffocation. _____

12. It appears that the dog had pushed its nose into the only air hole in the barrel, leaving Willard to perish! _____

> - Use the possessive form for a noun or pronoun that modifies a gerund. (For more on possessives, see Lesson 24.)
>
>    EXAMPLES: **Incorrect:** We were annoyed by **Glen** <u>trespassing</u> on our land.
>    **Correct:** We were annoyed by **Glen's** <u>trespassing</u> on our land.
>    **Incorrect:** We were annoyed by **them** <u>trespassing</u> on our land.
>    **Correct:** We were annoyed by **their** <u>trespassing</u> on our land.

**B. Underline the correct form of the noun or pronoun in parentheses.**

1. (Them, Their) calling to congratulate me really means a lot.

2. The trouble with (you, your) reading ahead is that you might spoil the ending for the rest of us.

3. I'm a bit in awe of (you, your) receiving a telegram from the Prime Minister.

4. My (father, father's) reading Robert Burns in a bad Scottish accent has become a tradition.

> - **Infinitive phrases** consist of the infinitive form of the verb along with any words that modify the infinitive. Infinitive phrases act as nouns, adjectives, or adverbs in a sentence.
>
>    EXAMPLES: **Nouns:** <u>To become a black belt</u> requires practice.
>    I love <u>to sing in the shower</u>.
>    **Adjective:** The best flour <u>to use for bread</u> is hard flour.
>    **Adverb:** You should rest <u>to recover your strength</u>.

**C. Underline each infinitive phrase, and then write the part of speech (adjective, adverb, or noun) that describes its function in the sentence.**

1. I brought some icing to put on the cake. _____

2. I put the wet towels on the clothesline to dry them out. _____

3. To stand up to a bully takes a lot of courage. _____

4. The quickest way to get to my house is by taking the sideroads. _____

> - It is sometimes useful to replace a long or wordy clause with a verbal phrase to make your writing tighter and more economical.
>
>    EXAMPLES: **Clause:** <u>When you write an essay</u>, don't forget <u>that you need to acknowledge your sources</u>.
>    **Verbal Phrase:** <u>When writing an essay</u>, don't forget <u>to acknowledge your sources</u>.

**D. Rephrase the following sentences in your notebook, replacing underlined clauses with verbal phrases. Other parts of the sentence may also change.**

1. This fellow claims <u>that he is the top-seeded badminton player in the city</u>.

2. The organizers decided <u>that they would let the concert continue</u>.

3. The only way <u>that we can change the world</u> is <u>if we change ourselves</u>.

4. <u>I was walking the dog</u>, and I ran into an old friend.

5. We were tired out <u>from our long walk</u> when we arrived at Ashanti's front door.

# Lesson 32 — Subject–Verb Agreement

- A verb must agree in number with its subject.
  EXAMPLES: **Raj** is making pancakes.   The **pancakes** are ready.
- Difficulties with subject–verb agreement arise in the situations that follow.

| Situation | Rule | Example (subject / verb) |
|---|---|---|
| Collective noun as subject | Usually, use a singular verb.<br><br>Use a plural verb if group members are acting independently. | The **audience** is clapping loudly.<br><br>The **audience** are taking their seats. |
| Indefinite pronoun as subject<br>(**Note**: Many indefinite pronouns can also function as adjectives when they directly precede a noun. In these cases, the verb agrees with the noun that follows the pronoun; e.g., Some **teeth** are missing.) | Usually use a singular verb, except with both, few, many, others, and several, which take a plural verb.<br><br>Use a singular or plural verb with all, any, none, more, most, or some, depending on the context. | **Everybody** is chipping in to buy a pizza.<br>**Many** of us have visited the West.<br><br>**Some** money is missing.<br>**Some** books are hard to find. |
| Compound subject connected by and | Usually use a plural verb.<br><br>Use a singular verb when the items form a single unit, or refer to the same person or thing. | **Sun and water** mean fun.<br><br>The **stars and stripes** is a symbol of the USA.<br>The **party leader and head of government** is the Prime Minister. |
| Compound subject connected by or or nor | Make the verb agree with the closest subject.<br><br>When one subject is plural and the other is singular, it usually sounds better to put the plural subject closer to the verb. | **Neither Eddie nor his parents** have seen their cat.<br><br>**A colourful scarf or gold earrings** transform an everyday outfit into something special. |

**A.** **Circle the correct singular or plural verb form given in parentheses.**

1. Erin and Paisley (is, are) competing in the biathlon at the track club.

2. The whole family (watches, watch) a video together every Friday night.

3. A columnist and long-time political observer (note, notes) that the government will have to act quickly to keep unemployment from rising.

4. Bacon and eggs (tastes, taste) great cooked over a campfire.

5. Some dogs (love, loves) to chase squirrels.

6. The team (was, were) signing autographs, handing out baseballs, and chatting with their fans.

7. Either social work or the healing professions (appeals, appeal) to me as a career.

> - When words separate the subject and the verb in a sentence, be sure to make the verb agree with the true subject. A noun or pronoun that is the object of a preposition (such as <u>in</u>, <u>of</u>, <u>by</u>, <u>through</u>, <u>with</u>, or <u>for</u>) cannot also be the subject of a sentence.
>
>    EXAMPLE:   A **family** of albino rabbits <u>lives</u> in the field. [subject is "family," not "rabbits"]
>
> - In sentences that begin with <u>there is</u> or <u>there are</u>, the subject is usually the noun or pronoun that follows the verb. If the subject is singular, use <u>is</u>; if it is plural, use <u>are</u>.
>
>    EXAMPLES:  There <u>is</u> **a grilled cheese sandwich** on the table for you.
>    There <u>are</u> **more DVDs** in the cupboard downstairs.

B.  **Circle the subject(s) and underline the verb(s) in the following sentences. Write <u>YES</u> if the subject and verb agree, or <u>NO</u> if they do not agree.**

   1.  Everyone living in these apartments and on nearby streets knows Bud, my pet snake. _____

   2.  All of the members of the festival committee feels proud of this year's festival. _____

   3.  Multiple fractures in my right arm has prevented me from skateboarding this summer. _____

   4.  There was a bag of sour milk and three mouldy carrots in the refrigerator. _____

   5.  There is a crowd of reporters outside the door. _____

   6.  Each of the elected members on the Board of Directors are expected to serve for two years. _____

   7.  There were a herd of antelopes grazing right in front of us. _____

   8.  Few of the courses offered at this college interest me. _____

   9.  One couple from New Brunswick who were en route to California was held up at the border for

       three hours. _____

   10. Most of the scenes in this otherwise boring movie are quite funny. _____

C.  **Write sentences to illustrate the descriptions given below. Use a verb in the present tense that agrees with the subject.**

   1.  [indefinite pronoun as the subject] _____

       _____

   2.  [collective noun as the subject] _____

       _____

   3.  [compound subject connected by <u>or</u> or <u>nor</u>] _____

       _____

Voice refers to the relation of a subject to the action expressed by the verb.

- In the **active voice**, the subject performs the action. In the **passive voice** (a form of <u>be</u> + past participle), the subject receives the action, or is acted upon.

    EXAMPLES: **Active:** The new owners <u>renovated</u> the house.
    **Passive:** The house <u>was renovated</u> by the new owners.

- In most cases, use the active voice. Only use the passive voice when the doer of the action is unknown, unimportant, or obvious. For example, the passive voice is often used in lab reports, because the experiment itself is more important than the person performing it.

    EXAMPLES: The blood samples <u>will be tested</u> for viruses.
    That player <u>has been known</u> to score four goals in one game.

**Rewrite each sentence in the active voice. If necessary, create a logical subject.**

1. Avalanches have been studied for years, but we still have a lot to learn about them.

2. In some cases, only the loose top layers of snow are carried down the mountain.

3. More damage is done by slab avalanches.

4. In fact, speeds of over 160 kilometres an hour can be reached by this type of avalanche.

5. During unconfined avalanches, the direction of the avalanche is determined by gravity alone.

6. By contrast, the path of a channelled avalanche is determined by canyons or other land formations.

7. In 1910, fifty-eight people were killed by a single avalanche in Roger's Pass, B.C.

8. Mountains with slopes of between 30° and 45° are most likely to produce avalanches.

9. Because of their keen sense of smell, dogs are often used to find avalanche victims.

10. An area the size of a football field can be searched by dogs in about twenty minutes.

- A **pronoun** is a word that replaces or stands for a noun or another pronoun. The categories of pronouns are as follows. Note that some pronouns appear in more than one category.

| Class | Examples | Use |
|---|---|---|
| Personal | I, you, he, she, it, we, they, me, him, her, us, them, mine, yours, his, hers, its, ours, theirs | replace the name of a person or thing (Amir explained how **he** fixed the car.) |
| Demonstrative | this, that, these, those | point to something (**Those** are my boots.) |
| Interrogative | who, whose, whom, which, what | to ask a question (**What** was that?) |
| Reflexive | myself, yourself, himself, herself, yourselves, ourselves, themselves | to intensify a noun or personal pronoun (I **myself** will show you the way.)<br><br>or to refer back to the subject (I made **myself** a cup of coffee.) |
| Relative | who, which, that | to introduce an adjective clause (The jeans **that** I want are low-cut.) |
| Indefinite | any, both, each, either, neither, none, all, one, few, some, anyone, somebody, everything, much, most | to indicate a vague, general, or unknown person or thing (**Somebody** left a pair of socks behind.) |

**Label each pronoun in the space above each line as personal (P), demonstrative (D), interrogative (INT), reflexive (RX), relative (RL), or indefinite (IND).**

1. Most of the cards that you buy in the stores have little rhymes inside.

2. That is the funniest joke I've ever heard.

3. The doctor himself advised you to take time off.

4. Who would be knocking on the door so late at night?

5. She told herself everything would be fine.

6. Are these the walls they want us to paint?

7. Wild coy-dogs (which are part coyote, part dog) often prowl around farms and steal chickens.

8. None of the buildings remained standing, but everyone got out before they collapsed.

9. We drive the same make of car, but mine is blue and yours is silver.

10. You lose much of the nutrition in lettuce if you cut it with a steel blade.

## Lesson 35 — Pronoun Antecedents

- An **antecedent** is a word or words that a pronoun refers back to or replaces. Pronouns and antecedents must be in agreement. This rule also applies to possessive adjectives, such as <u>her</u>, <u>their</u>, and <u>its</u>.

    EXAMPLES: **Maria** admits <u>she</u> is tired.
    **The Samsons** gave Ted <u>their</u> lawn mower.

**A. Use arrows to connect pronouns and antecedents in the following sentences.**

1. Pia admired Dave's pen, so he gave it to her.

2. Shane's new motorcycle had a flat, so he left it in the garage.

3. Lacy told Robert not to eat the chips until she had some.

4. The frog flicked its tongue, and the mosquito disappeared into its mouth.

- **Indefinite pronouns** that take a singular verb (for example, <u>each</u>, <u>either</u>, <u>neither</u>, <u>none</u>, or <u>one</u>, as well as pronouns ending in -body, -one, or -thing) also take a singular pronoun or pronoun adjective.

    EXAMPLES: **Incorrect: Each** of the VJs has <u>their</u> own style. [singular
    **antecedent** and plural <u>pronoun</u>]
    **Correct: Each** of the VJs has <u>his or her</u> own style. [both
    singular]
    **Correct: All** of the VJs have <u>their</u> own styles. [both plural]

**B. Fill in each blank space with a pronoun that agrees with the indefinite pronoun. Unless the context suggests otherwise, assume the people referred to are both male and female.**

1. None of my friends had _____ cell phone.

2. Several of the caged animals bared _____ teeth at me.

3. If everyone picked up _____ own garbage, this school would look a lot better.

4. Most of the class has already given _____ presentations.

5. Each of my brothers plays goalie for _____ hockey team.

6. Someone left _____ keys in the TV room.

- When the antecedent is a **collective noun**, you have two choices. If the group is acting as one unit, use a singular pronoun to refer to it. If the group members are acting individually, use a plural pronoun.

    EXAMPLES: The **audience** expressed <u>its</u> approval. [acting as a unit]
    The **audience** wiped <u>their</u> eyes and blew <u>their</u> noses. [acting as
    individuals]

---

**Unit 3, Grammar and Usage**
© 2004 Gage Learning Corporation
**57**

**C. Circle the personal pronoun that agrees with the antecedent. Underline the antecedent.**

1. A flock of starlings gathers outside my window each morning and sings (its, their) wake-up song at high decibels.

2. A bunch of bananas hung in the tree until Asher chopped (it, them) down.

3. The committee agreed to meet again in two months, after (its, their) holidays were over.

4. The class was given (its, their) first big assignment this week.

5. The team held out (its, their) hands for the traditional handshake after the game.

6. The jury could not speak to anyone, including (its, their) loved ones, until the trial ended.

---

- The antecedents of the pronouns you use must be clear to your reader.
- Be particularly careful when using the pronouns it, this, and that, which are often mistakenly used without a clear antecedent.

    EXAMPLES: **Vague:** The driving instructor wanted me to postpone my road test so I could perfect my parallel parking. I told her that would not be easy. [Would postponing the road test be difficult, or practising parallel parking?]

    **Revised:** I told her postponing the test would not be easy.

    **Revised:** I told her that perfecting my parallel parking would not be easy.

---

**D. Rewrite the following sentences to make the pronoun antecedent clear.**

1. The old sci-fi movie showed scenes of a huge creature with green scales rising out of a lagoon and terrorizing a town. It was soon destroyed.

_____

_____

2. Many retired Canadians go to Florida every winter, following the example of migrating birds that need to escape the cold. These are known as "snowbirds."

_____

_____

3. I went to get the dictionary to find out the meaning of the word, but it was not there.

_____

_____

4. The film *O Brother, Where Art Thou?* is an artful retelling of *The Odyssey*, Homer's epic tale of the journey of Odysseus. It is set in the southern United States in the 1930s.

_____

_____

# Relative and Reflexive Pronouns

> - A **relative pronoun** introduces a subordinate clause that functions as an adjective. These clauses are sometimes called **relative clauses**. <u>Who</u>, <u>whom</u>, <u>whose</u>, <u>which</u>, and <u>that</u> can all function as relative pronouns. The antecedent of a relative pronoun is always a noun or pronoun in the main clause.
>   - EXAMPLE: **Immigrants** <u>whose first language is neither English nor French</u> are called allophones in Québec. [antecedent of <u>whose</u> is "Immigrants"]
> - Sometimes, two sentences can be combined by changing the less important sentence into a relative clause.
>   - EXAMPLE: **Two Sentences:** My first bike is still in my parents' garage. It had training wheels and ribbons on the handlebars.
>   - **Combined:** My first bike, <u>which is still in my parents' garage</u>, had training wheels and ribbons on the handlebars. [antecedent of <u>which</u> is "bike"]

**A. Rewrite the following passage in your notebook. Combine sentences by changing one sentence from each pair to a relative clause.**

Alexander became the king of Macedonia in the fourth century B.C.E. He was nicknamed "The Great." Although he reigned for only thirteen years, he created a vast empire. His empire included virtually all of the known world at the time. Alexander's leadership and charisma were legendary. He was one of the last great military commanders to lead the charge into every battle himself. He encouraged the intermarriage of Greeks and Persians. According to some historians, this fact makes Alexander one of the first leaders to actively promote the peaceful co-existence of different cultures. He also made economic reforms. These reforms endured until the nineteenth century.

> - Use **reflexive pronouns** (<u>myself</u>, <u>yourself</u>, etc.) to refer back to a person or thing that is the subject of the sentence, or to add emphasis to a noun or pronoun.
>   - EXAMPLES: **Zoe** hummed to <u>herself</u> as she navigated the deadly rapids.
>     This copy of the book is signed by the **author** <u>herself</u>.
> - Never use a reflexive pronoun in place of a personal pronoun.
>   - EXAMPLE: **Incorrect:** Janice and **myself** are going fishing tomorrow.
>     **Correct:** Janice and **I** are going fishing tomorrow.

**B. Underline the reflexive pronoun in each sentence. Write C if it is used correctly. If it is used incorrectly, write the pronoun that should replace it.**

1. Khan was standing beside the great man himself! _____

2. Anika cooked herself an egg. _____

3. Ferenc gave everyone but yourself a big serving of dessert. _____

4. Shanice and myself are going to the mall. _____

5. Don't be so hard on yourself! _____

## Pronoun Case

> - Some pronouns have different forms, or cases, to indicate their function. The three cases of pronouns are subjective, objective, and possessive.
> - Use **subjective pronouns** (I, you, he, she, it, we, they, who) as the subject or subject complement in a clause or sentence.
>
>   EXAMPLES: Omar and I stick together.
>   It was he who dropped the glass.
>   I forgot that they were coming.
>
> - Use **objective pronouns** (me, you, him, her, it, us, them, whom) as direct and indirect objects, or as objects of prepositions.
>
>   EXAMPLES: Mimi beat them all at table tennis. [direct object]
>   Oliver gave him a note. [indirect object]
>   Min made supper for us. [object of preposition]
>
> - Use **possessive pronouns** (mine, yours, his, hers, its, ours, theirs, whose) to indicate possession.
>
>   EXAMPLE: When Todd took the last meatball, he didn't realize it was yours.
>
> **Note:** My, your, his, her, our, their, and whose used before a noun are possessive adjectives, not pronouns (see Lesson 39).

**A. Circle the correct form of the personal pronoun in parentheses, and then identify its case as subjective (S), objective (O), or possessive (P).**

1. Nina and (I, me) got our hair cut at the same salon. _____

2. I suppose that shadowy figure might have been (he, him), but I can't be sure. _____

3. I've seen blue eyes, but (her's, hers) are bluer than anyone else's. _____

4. Dagmar expected Helena and (they, them) to help pay for the barbecue. _____

5. (They, Them) and their friends are going camping together next spring. _____

6. Jonah took (they, them) and their kids to Assiniboine Park. _____

7. They are coming over to watch TV with us, because (their, theirs) is broken. _____

8. I found out that (she, her) and her brother were twins. _____

9. Kira bought tickets for Bill and (she, her). _____

10. Neither Max nor (he, him) can play basketball. _____

> - A pronoun that follows <u>than</u> or <u>as</u> can be in the subjective or objective case, depending on the context. To determine which case is required, fill in the missing words in the second clause.
>
>   EXAMPLES: Paul spoke to Vanessa longer than (he spoke to) me. ["me" is the object of the preposition <u>to</u>, so use objective case]
>
>   Paul spoke to Vanessa longer than I (spoke to her). ["I" is subject of the clause <u>than I spoke to her</u>, so use the subjective case]

**B. Circle the correct form of the pronoun given in parentheses.**

1. Chantal plays fiddle better than (I, me).

2. That sweater is looser on you than on (he, him).

3. The others enjoyed the book more than (I, me).

4. My dad was once a big Beatles fan; back then, no one liked the Fab Four as much as (he, him).

5. Boris was upset because he thought I was ignoring him; he said I talked to everyone else at the party more than (he, him).

6. Sometimes I think you like your snowboard as much as (I, me), which doesn't say much for our relationship!

7. That jacket suits Ishan more than (he, him).

8. I could never drink as many soft drinks at one sitting as (she, her)!

9. None of the other groups who presented were better than (they, them).

10. Our dog, Fido, likes Judy better than (I, me), because Judy takes him for more walks.

> - Writers and speakers sometimes express solidarity with a particular group by using a noun directly preceded by <u>we</u> or <u>us</u> (as in "we the people" or "us farmers"). In expressions like these, the pronoun case is the same as it would be without the noun.
>
>   EXAMPLE: **Incorrect:** <u>Us workers</u> want higher wages. ["Us want" is incorrect.]
>
>   **Correct:** <u>We workers</u> want higher wages. ["We want" is correct.]

**C. Write <u>we</u> or <u>us</u> in the blank.**

1. Joining a food co-operative gives _____ consumers more control over prices.

2. _____ joggers have bad knees but healthy hearts.

3. It is important that _____ voters exercise our franchise!

4. The thing about _____ rugby players is that we are tougher than everyone else!

5. Rising tuition fees are hurting _____ poor students who have to work our way through school.

# Lesson

## 38     Using Who/Whom and Whose/Who's

---

- Use **who** for the subjective case, and **whom** for the objective case. Who and whom are often used interchangeably in informal speech, but be sure to use the correct case in written work and in more formal speaking situations.

    EXAMPLE: **Incorrect/Informal:** Who would you like to speak with? [Whom is the object of the preposition with, so requires the objective case]

    **Correct/Formal:** Whom would you like to speak with?

---

**A. Complete each sentence in correct style for formal writing using either who or whom.**

1. Many members of the original Monty Python comedy team, _____ were all extremely funny, have had successful comedy careers in their own right.

2. With _____ are you going to the graduation dinner?

3. _____ told you the secret, and _____ did you tell?

4. I thanked the lifeguard _____ saved my life.

5. A classmate _____ I had not seen since junior high came up to me to say hello.

6. People _____ walk their dogs in the park should clean up their mess.

7. The artist _____ produced this CD really knew what she was doing.

8. _____ are you waiting for?

9. You got a card from _____ ?

10. The guy in the picture is _____ ?

---

- **Whose** is the possessive case of who or which.

    EXAMPLES: Whose are those running shoes?    I don't know whose they are.

- Use **who's** as a contraction for who is or who has, but never as a possessive.

    EXAMPLES: She's the woman who's standing in front of you.

    Who's heard from Stan recently?

---

**B. Write who's or whose on the line to complete each sentence correctly.**

1. _____ taken the ketchup?

2. Everyone _____ going to college next year, raise your hand.

3. _____ turn is it to do the dishes?

4. Not everyone _____ first choice is to live in residence will be accepted.

5. A friend of mine _____ going tree planting this summer asked me to go along.

---

# Lesson
## 39

> Adjectives and adverbs are modifiers; they add colour, precision, and clarity to nouns, verbs, and other words.
>
> - **Adjectives** describe, identify, or limit a noun or pronoun. The largest group of adjectives is known as **descriptive adjectives**. Words that are normally classified as nouns are sometimes used as descriptive adjectives. So are some verb forms.
>
>   EXAMPLES: big, black birds    bus route    holding pattern
>             wild blue yonder    system failure    spilled milk
>
> - Pronouns that precede a noun are called **possessive adjectives**.
>
>   EXAMPLES: his collar    that house    their backyard    whose ring
>
> - The adjectives the, a, and an are called **articles**.

**A. Underline all the adjectives in the following sentences.**

1. My first two times at bat, I struck out.

2. I ate three delicious pastries, and the last one really did me in!

3. She has two piercings in each ear.

4. That hat trick was a first for me.

5. Those adorable sheep belong in a petting zoo!

6. Tell me which pair of blue shoes looks best, in your opinion.

7. Some intrepid performers climbed the steep ladder to the flying trapeze.

8. Those scented candles are going to be part of our next fundraising project.

9. Two lucky students will be representing our school in Germany next month.

10. The donation boxes will be placed on all the street corners in the entire city.

11. My car battery dies every time I turn off the engine.

12. The local hardware store does not have any painting supplies.

13. An elderly servant brought their lunch into the elegant drawing room.

14. This hotel suite can accommodate all seven people?

15. Sandi Gupta gave a rousing valedictory speech at our graduation ceremony.

- **Adverbs** modify a verb, an adjective, another adverb, or a whole clause. They tell <u>how</u>, <u>when</u>, <u>where</u>, <u>why</u>, <u>to what extent</u>, or <u>how often</u>. Many, but not all, adverbs end in -ly.

  EXAMPLES: The police officer spoke <u>quietly</u>. [modifies verb "spoke"]
  That was a <u>pretty</u> hard test. [modifies adjective "hard"]
  Rachel runs <u>very</u> fast. [modifies adverb "fast"]
  <u>Clearly</u>, nothing had changed. [modifies the whole clause]

**B.** Underline the words that are adjectives and circle the words that are adverbs in each of the following sentences.

1. The warm sun and gently lapping waves soon relaxed me.

2. Fortunately, I always remember to lock the front door securely.

3. A balanced diet will make you live longer and feel healthy.

4. Her first solo exhibition was held in the overly ornate foyer of a very famous gallery.

5. Apparently, improperly cooked meat can be extremely poisonous.

- Use an adjective to modify a linking verb. Use an adverb to modify an action verb.

  EXAMPLES: You **look** <u>sad</u>. [<u>look</u> is a linking verb here, so use an adjective]
  Johanna **looked** <u>sadly</u> at the wilted flowers. [<u>looked</u> is an action verb here, so use an adverb]

- While <u>well</u> can be an adjective (referring to health) or an adverb, <u>good</u> is only used as an adjective.

  EXAMPLES: **Incorrect:** I play guitar good.
  **Correct:** I play guitar well. [adverb <u>well</u> modifies action verb "play"]
  **Correct:** I am good at guitar [adjective <u>good</u> modifies linking verb "am"]

**C.** Choose the correct modifier from those given in parentheses.

1. The band felt (good, well) about their new album.

2. Those pants look (loose, loosely) on you.

3. I don't feel (good, well).

4. Jenna writes (good, well).

5. I held his hand (tight, tightly).

**D.** Find colourful, descriptive adjectives and adverbs to add to or replace modifiers in the following sentences. Write the revised sentences in your notebook.

1. The sky reminded us that we had better get home.

2. The car was red.

3. I sat against a tree and gazed at the forest around me.

4. The dog growled and bared its fangs.

5. The ideas in this novel are interesting, but the writing is boring.

# Comparing with Adjectives and Adverbs

- Use -er to form the comparative (colder, harder) and -est to form the superlative (coldest, hardest) of most **adjectives** of one syllable and some of two syllables. Longer adjectives usually use <u>more</u> (or <u>less</u>) to form the comparative, and <u>most</u> (or <u>least</u>) to form the superlative.

  EXAMPLES: cold      colder          coldest
             radiant      more (less) radiant      most (least) radiant

- Most **adverbs**, especially those ending in -ly, use more (or less) to form the comparative, and most (or least) to form the superlative.

  EXAMPLES: carefully      more (less) carefully      most (least) carefully

- Some common adjectives and adverbs have irregular comparative and superlative forms.

  EXAMPLES: good/well      better      best
             bad/badly      worse      worst
             little (adv.)      less      least
             many/much      more      most

- When comparing two things or people, use the comparative; use the superlative only when comparing more than two people or things.

  EXAMPLES: Ayanna is more fluent in French than Kyla.
             Ayanna is the most fluent French-speaker in the class.

**Correct any errors in the use of the comparative or superlative. Use proofreader's marks.**

1. This is the friendlier class I have ever been in.

2. If I had to choose between pizza and macaroni and cheese, I'd say pizza was the most good.

3. I downloaded this version of the file easier than the other.

4. I think that scenario is the less probable of the three we discussed.

5. Of the four of us, Donald contributed littlest to the project.

6. Most people approved of the merger than disapproved.

7. Dana is our more competent employee, so she supervises the others.

8. You are looking more well since you got home from the hospital.

9. We need to go quicklier if we want to get home before dark.

10. Albert is less angrier than Wes.

## Conjunctions and Conjunctive Adverbs

---

A **conjunction** is a word used to join words or groups of words together.

- The **co-ordinating conjunctions** <u>and</u>, <u>but</u>, <u>yet</u>, <u>so</u>, <u>or</u>, <u>for</u>, and <u>nor</u> join two or more words, phrases, or clauses of equal rank in a sentence.

    EXAMPLE:   Chloe wanted to leave, but Matt convinced her to stay.

- **Subordinating conjunctions**, such as <u>although</u>, <u>because</u>, <u>while</u>, <u>since</u>, <u>when</u>, and <u>if</u>, join elements of unequal rank in a sentence.

    EXAMPLE:   Although I was very hot, I kept on walking.

- **Correlative conjunctions**, such as <u>not only…but also</u>, <u>either…or</u>, <u>neither…nor</u>, and <u>both…and</u>, join two equal parts of a sentence.

    EXAMPLES: Louis not only goes to school, but also has a part-time job.
    They found my embarrassment both funny and touching.

---

**A.   Underline the conjunction in each sentence. Then, identify it on the line as co-ordinating (C), subordinating (S), or correlative (CR).**

1. Calvin and Juliet attended the job fair together in the school auditorium. _____

2. Neither the plant manager nor the workers know how to operate the new machine. _____

3. If the bingo hall is closed, several charities will suffer. _____

4. The hiring committee interviewed ten candidates, but has not made a decision. _____

5. We can either take a trip or buy a new car. _____

---

- **Conjunctive adverbs**, such as <u>consequently</u>, <u>furthermore</u>, <u>hence</u>, and <u>however</u>, can be used like a conjunction at the beginning of a sentence, or between two independent clauses joined by a semicolon. Never use a conjunctive adverb alone to join clauses.

    EXAMPLE: **Incorrect:** I would love a laptop, however, they cost too much.
    **Correct:** I would love a laptop; however, they cost too much.

---

**B.   Improve the flow of the following passage by adding a total of five conjunctions and conjunctive adverbs. Revise the punctuation as necessary. Use proofreader's marks to make the changes.**

The recent budget cuts have reduced our funding. We have had to discontinue some programs. We will

continue to offer our employment skills program. The résumé-writing workshops scheduled for next month

will go ahead as planned. We hope to raise funds through private donations. We will once again be able to

offer a full slate of programs. Please bear with us, as we do our best to meet your needs.

---

# Prepositions

> - A **preposition** is a word that shows the relationship between words or phrases in a sentence. Here are some common prepositions:
>
> EXAMPLES:
>
> | among | between | from | on | toward |
> |-------|---------|------|-----|--------|
> | at | by | in | over | under |
> | around | during | into | through | with |
> | behind | for | of | to | within |
>
> We took the dog **to** the vet **on** Saturday **for** a checkup.

**A. Underline the prepositions in the following passage.**

In a recent study, scientists found that when the cold virus was dropped directly into the nasal passage, almost all subjects became infected. But only three-quarters of those with the infection developed a cold. Nobody really knows why some subjects did not seem to get any symptoms from the virus. One thing is certain, though; all Canadians will suffer through a cold at least once during their lifetime. The only good news is that most colds are gone within a week. **[10 prepositions]**

> - Use <u>between</u> to refer to two people, groups, or things; use <u>among</u> to refer to more than two.
> - Use <u>different from</u> in most instances. Use <u>different than</u> only to avoid awkward phrasing, especially when what follows is a clause.

**B. Choose the correct preposition from the pair in parentheses.**

1. The lottery grand prize will be distributed (between, among) six lucky cafeteria workers.

2. My painting turned out much different (from, than) I had expected.

3. The wind blowing (between, among) the trees made a pleasant sound.

4. Cathy used her Global Positioning System device to calculate the distance (between, among) her house and the school.

5. Kendra divides her time (between, among) Vancouver and St. John's.

6. This movie is different (than, from) any other martial arts movie I've seen.

> - If you are trying to speak or write formally, it is usually best to avoid ending a sentence with a preposition.
>   - EXAMPLE: **Informal:** Whom shall I give the message to?
>   **Formal:** To whom shall I give the message?
> - However, if following this rule makes the sentence sound more awkward, it is better to leave it or reword the sentence.
>   - EXAMPLE: **Awkward:** That is the school to which I used to go.
>   **Reworded:** That is the school I used to attend.

**C. Rearrange or reword the following sentences in your notebook to eliminate the preposition at the end.**

1. Listen to the noise I have to put up with!

2. Whom was this story written by?

3. St. Mark's is the most prestigious of all the colleges I have applied to.

4. I have heard nothing from the person I wrote to.

# Lesson 43

## Prepositional Phrases

- A **prepositional phrase** is a group of words that begins with a preposition and ends with a noun or pronoun, called the **object of the preposition**. Prepositional phrases usually act as adjectives or adverbs in a sentence.
- The word the prepositional phrase modifies is called its antecedent. If the antecedent is a noun, the phrase is acting as an adjective. If the **antecedent** is a verb, the phrase is acting as an adverb.

  EXAMPLES: **Adjective:** $\underset{\text{antecedent}}{\underline{\text{Tickets}}}$ $\underset{\text{prep. phrase}}{\textbf{for the show}}$ are sold out.

  **Adverbs:** I $\underset{\text{antecedent}}{\underline{\text{will go}}}$ $\underset{\text{prep. phrase}}{\textbf{on holidays}}$ next week.

  Tom $\underset{\text{antecedent}}{\underline{\text{starts}}}$ his day $\underset{\text{prep. phrase}}{\textbf{at six}}$.

**A. Underline each prepositional phrase once, and draw an arrow to its antecedent. In the space above, write ADJ if the phrase functions as an adjective, or ADV if it functions as an adverb in the sentence.**

1. I looked toward the horizon, but could see no land.

2. Lucianna told her parents about her new job.

3. We need two more players for our brass quintet.

4. Carrie takes aikido classes after school.

5. The show that I saw about black holes will air again tomorrow night.

6. My uncle made a film about Newfoundland and Labrador.

7. Mr. Ng laughed quietly to himself.

8. Stavros scolded his dog for chewing the furniture.

9. The cover of her latest book really stands out.

- Look for opportunities to make your writing more concise by replacing subordinate clauses with prepositional phrases.

  EXAMPLE: **Clause:** Most students who are in my class are away this week.
  **Phrase:** Most students in my class are away this week.

**B. Revise the following passage by replacing six subordinate clauses with prepositional phrases.**

The contestants who appear on reality TV programs will do anything to win. If they don't have a killer

instinct, they don't last long. This usually means that the contestants who have the best chance of winning

are the ones you hope don't make it! It is astounding what people will do if they think they can get easy

money. What other crazy "reality" concepts will they bring us when they unveil the new television season?

(Of course, I only watch these shows because I like the commercials.)

## Lesson 44 — Double Negatives

- A **double negative** occurs when two negative elements are used in a sentence. The two negatives cancel each other to make a positive.

- The negative elements used may include <u>not</u> along with an adverb such as <u>hardly</u>, <u>scarcely</u>, <u>nothing</u>, or <u>never</u>. This type of double negative is usually used by mistake in place of a negative statement. To correct it, remove one of the negative elements.

  EXAMPLES: **Double Negative:** I can't see nothing. [= I can see something.]
  **Correct:** I can't see anything.
  **Correct:** I can see nothing.

**A. Rewrite each sentence to eliminate the double negative.**

1. I don't believe none of those reports. _____

2. I haven't had hardly any mosquito bites. _____

3. I can't barely get this coat zipped up any more. _____

4. I haven't no patience for red tape. _____

5. Donna won't never forget what happened. _____

- Another form of double negative uses a negative word such as <u>not</u> with a negative prefix, such as un-, dis-, or de-. Writers sometimes use these constructions on purpose.

  EXAMPLE:  I don't entirely disbelieve your story. [= I partly believe your story.]

**B. Write a positive statement by removing the two negative elements in each of the following sentences.**

1. We don't disapprove of your behaviour. _____

2. The higher court didn't disagree with the judge's ruling. _____

3. Paolo's departure was not unexpected. _____

4. Keisha was not unhappy about moving to Edmonton. _____

5. The plan you propose is not unappealing. _____

**C. In your notebook, describe how the connotation of the positive statements you wrote in Part B differs from that of the double negatives. Why do you think a writer might purposely choose to use double negatives like these?**

# Misplaced and Dangling Modifiers

- A **misplaced modifier** is a word or phrase that appears to modify the wrong word. To avoid misplaced modifiers, position modifying words or phrases as close as possible to the word they modify.

  EXAMPLE: **Misplaced:** Di showed me the report that she wrote <u>on trees</u>.
  **Correct:** Di showed me the report <u>on trees</u> that she wrote.

- A **dangling modifier** modifies a word that is implied, but not actually stated, in the sentence. Dangling modifiers are a common error in sentences beginning with a modifying phrase. To fix a dangling modifier, you may have to rephrase the sentence.

  EXAMPLE: **Dangling:** <u>Feeling ill</u>, the doctors could find nothing wrong.
  **Correct:** <u>Although I felt ill</u>, the doctors could find nothing wrong.

**Rewrite the following sentences to avoid misplaced or dangling modifiers.**

1. With flapping wings, I watched as two gulls fought over some fish.

   _____

2. Hoping to catch the mouse, a trap baited with cheese was left under the sink.

   _____

3. Gathering strength, meteorologists warned that the tropical storm might become a hurricane.

   _____

4. Sam did research about solar eclipses on the Internet.

   _____

5. I noticed my parents standing at the back of the hall while receiving my diploma.

   _____

6. Unable to swim, the lifeguard warned me not to go in the water alone.

   _____

7. Carlson was shredding papers when the detective came in to destroy the evidence.

   _____

8. Cooked to perfection, I sat down to a delicious breakfast.

   _____

9. Daphne burned the note that the mail carrier had left in the woodstove.

   _____

10. Overjoyed at being rescued, the helicopter landed beside our makeshift camp.

   _____

# Lesson 46 — Parallel Structure

> ■ Writing that is **parallel** uses similar grammatical patterns of words, phrases, or clauses. Sentences with parallel structure sound rhythmic and balanced. Elements that are parallel should have the same level of importance.
>
> ■ Items in a list or series should be parallel.
>
> EXAMPLES: The colours of the crest are black, green, and blue. [adjectives]
> The colours of the crest are black for death, green for life, and blue for loyalty. [phrases]
>
> ■ Words following two parts of a correlative conjunction (either...or, neither...nor, not only...but also) should also be parallel.
>
> EXAMPLES: Either we should leave now, or we should wait until tomorrow [clauses]
> We should either leave now, or wait until tomorrow. [phrases]

**A. Use proofreader's marks to improve the parallel structure of the following sentences.**

1. Neither talking on the phone nor e-mail gets quite the same results as speaking to someone in person.

2. Those shoes are not only out of fashion, but they are also too small for me.

3. I've both invited Andrea and her brother to join our aerobics class.

4. I have three goals in life: to complete my education, travelling around the world, and to run in the Boston Marathon.

5. The government will either increase our funding or they will cut the program altogether.

6. Satellites are used for many purposes, including

   • telecommunications

   • infrared photography

   • taking pictures of space

7. Because of the virus, St. Stephen's hospital administration has decided to close the Emergency ward temporarily and that ambulances will be diverted to other hospitals nearby.

8. You can both do the research and you can write a first draft in one weekend if you set your mind to it.

9. Not only am I going to pass the test, but also get the best mark in the class.

10. Neither the politician's family nor was she herself prepared for the media blitz that followed her election.

> - Use parallel structure in headings of an essay, report, or set of instructions to show topics that are related, or of equal importance.
> - Use parallel structure in bulleted or numbered lists.

**B. Use what you have learned about parallel structure to revise the following list of job skills from a résumé.**

- restocking shelves _____

- inventory _____

- customer service _____

- communicated with management _____

- creation of window displays _____

**C. Use your knowledge of parallel structure to improve the following outline. Make sure the main headings are expressed in parallel form, and that each group of subheadings also has a parallel grammatical structure.**

I. Doing Market Research _____

   - do surveys _____

   - databases _____

   - consulting focus groups _____

II. How to Develop a Product _____

   - the prototype _____

   - consider field testing _____

III. Creation of a Business Plan _____

   - get financing _____

   - doing market analysis _____

   - how to find suppliers _____

IV. Promote the Product _____

   - who is your target market? _____

   - publicity _____

   - providing customer service _____

**D. Find two other examples of the use of parallel structure in advertisements, articles, speeches, or persuasive or argumentative writing. In your notebook, explain why you think the examples you chose are effective.**

# Review

**A.** Match the underlined words with one of the descriptions given in the box. Write the letter that appears beside the description in the square brackets.

| | |
|---|---|
| a) interrogative pronoun | f) present participle |
| b) action verb | g) co-ordinating conjunction |
| c) linking verb | h) gerund |
| d) preposition | i) indefinite pronoun |
| e) pronoun adjective | j) relative pronoun |

1. Skating [ ] is prohibited without a skating [ ] pass.

2. Most [ ] Canadians have learned to make the most [ ] of our winter weather.

3. When I tasted [ ] the shellfish, I thought it tasted [ ] a little off.

4. For [ ] goodness sake, watch yourself on the stairs, for [ ] the handrail is broken.

5. Who [ ] is the mysterious character who [ ] waits in the shadows?


**B.** Circle the correct word from the choices in parentheses.

1. Seven dollars cannot be divided equally (between, among) twelve people.

2. Lina and (I, myself) agreed to attend the next board meeting.

3. The entire cast (has, have) arrived for the awards ceremony.

4. I cannot understand why (him, his) leaving for a few days should make you so upset.

5. A raccoon left (its, it's, its') footprints in the snow around my garbage bins.

6. Mr. Driscoll, (who, whom) we used to call Mr. D., has moved back to Ireland.

7. (Whose, Who's) boots are in the middle of the front hall?

8. Don't forget that before 1949, (we, us) Newfoundlanders were not part of Canada.

9. You will always be two years older than (I, me).

10. You look no (different from, different than) when we last met.

11. Could it have been (she, her) who arranged for my promotion?

12. I knocked on Sal and Dina (Franchetto's, Franchettos') door.

13. Anyone travelling through to Windsor should present (his or her, their) ticket to the conductor.

14. (There is, There are) room for three more people in this row.

15. The team left the ice with (its head, their heads) held high.

**C.** **Underline all the words that make up the main verb, and then write its tense on the line.**

1. Roger has been talking on the phone for two hours! _____

2. Tomorrow, Wilda will have been away for a week. _____

3. Sean was standing in the kitchen with an eggbeater in his hand. _____

4. Our Moscow office has agreed to consider the proposal seriously. _____

5. Maxine had never been invited to my family's cottage before. _____

**D.** **Underline all the verbals in the following sentences. Then, identify each in the space above as a gerund (G), participle (P), or infinitive (I).**

1. To become a skilled tradesperson, you will need to apprentice for many years.

2. Running a large manufacturing company is easy compared with organizing a family vacation!

3. A few words whispered in the ear of the DJ was all it took to get him to play our song.

4. Pina told me that the way to make mouth-watering chili is by adding ground cumin.

5. Whistling, Basil walked his dog among the neatly planted rows of trees in the park.

**E.** **Use proofreader's marks to correct any grammatical or usage errors.**

1. Either we increase our revenues, or our expenses will have to go down.

2. Snow-capped and treacherous, many climbers have met their doom on this mountain.

3. I don't hardly think he meant it when he said I had the job.

4. Don't you think the movie would have been more good if the director had quickened the pace?

5. The novel contains many gripping passages, however, the ending did not hold my attention.

6. Agathe Desrosiers is co-author of a book about decorating with my aunt.

**F.** **Rewrite the following sentences to change them from active voice to passive voice.**

1. The habitat of grizzly bears in this area has been drastically reduced by logging.

_____

2. The term "scrum" is used by the media to describe the crowd of reporters around a politician.

_____

3. The year 1816 was called the year with no summer by residents of Québec.

_____

4. That year, the region was hit by a major snowstorm in June, and crops were killed by an early frost at the beginning of August.

_____

**A.** Use proofreader's marks to find and correct the following grammatical errors in the passage below.

- one example of an incorrect reflexive pronoun
- one incorrect use of a plural pronoun to refer to a singular antecedent
- one example of incorrect pronoun case
- one example of incorrect subject–verb agreement
- one example of incorrect verb tense
- one example of incorrect use of adjectives
- one dangling modifier
- one example of an incorrect possessive form
- one double negative
- one incorrect use of a preposition

Have you ever wondered why a ten-dollar bill is worth less than a one-hundred-dollar bill? After all, the paper used to make the ten is no different than that used in the larger bills. The fact is, money only has value if people like yourself who are using it agree that it has value. So, if all of us suddenly decide tomorrow not to accept ten-dollar bills, the bills will, in fact, be worthless! By contrast, if us money spenders all at once agreed that playing cards were equivalent to ten-dollar bills, then a full deck would actually be worth $520!

In fact, you may be surprised to learn that playing cards were actually used as money for a while in New France. During the winter of 1685, the ship from France that was carrying a new supply of French coins did not arrive. The intendant, or governor, of the colony needed money really bad. He didn't hardly have enough to meet government expenses, so he took matters into his own hands. He cut up playing cards into four pieces, and wrote a value on the back of each. The government's wax seal was imprinted on each one, and there it was—instant money! When the ship finally does arrive with it's cargo of coins, each of the playing cards were redeemed for their face value. Pleased with this clever solution, playing-card money was issued several times by the French government in the years that followed.

**B.** **Increase the level of formality of the following passage by making these changes (use proofreader's marks):**

- **eliminate two sentences ending with a preposition**
- **replace a conjunction with a conjunctive adverb**
- **eliminate an incorrect use of <u>who</u> or <u>whom</u>**

The British, who took over the colony from the French after the battle of the Plains of Abraham, had a different monetary system. But French coins continued to circulate, along with the new British currency. At the same time, US coins were introduced by the American traders who the British conducted business with. Even Spanish coins, called "pieces of eight," ended up in the colony from time to time. All of these coins were accepted as legal currency, which people could buy goods with.

**C.** **Improve the style of the following passage by making these changes (use proofreader's marks):**

- **combine two sentences using a relative clause**
- **replace a subordinate clause with a verbal phrase**
- **improve parallel structure**
- **replace a subordinate clause with a prepositional phrase**
- **replace passive voice with active voice**
- **correct a dangling modifier**

I travelled with Nancy. She is an experienced backpacker. The sun was shining, which made the water look intensely blue. We walked up a trail into the mountains, stopping to look more closely at interesting plants, to consult the trail map, or catching our breath. When we had been walking for about half an hour, we came to an open section of the trail. I looked back the way we had come. My breath was taken away by the scene spread out below me. Calling to Nancy, we both stood looking down for a while, lost in our own thoughts.

## Commas

- The **comma** is used more often than any other punctuation mark. Using commas correctly can help a reader work out the meaning of a complicated sentence. The chart below lists some of its more common uses.

| Uses | Examples |
|---|---|
| to separate three or more items in a series | thunder, lightning, and hail |
| to separate two independent clauses in a compound sentence<br>**Note:** If both clauses are short, the comma may be omitted. | Jake wrote me a letter on Friday, and it arrived on Tuesday.<br>Traffic was slow but here we are. |
| to separate clauses in a complex sentence if the subordinate clause comes first | Because you left early, you missed the best part of the show. |
| to separate the day, month, and year in a complete date (note that a comma follows the year as well) | I submitted my report on Tuesday, March 4, 2003, at two o'clock in the afternoon. |
| to separate the name of a city from a province or country (note that a comma follows the province or country as well) | I live in Brandon, Manitoba.<br>We visited Vancouver, Canada, last summer. |
| to set off non-essential information, including introductory and non-restrictive words, phrases, and clauses (see Lesson 19) | Unfortunately, we got lost.<br>I met Raoul the other day, by the way.<br>The play, which closed yesterday, got poor reviews |
| to set off direct quotations from words identifying the speaker | The guide told us, "This is the oldest building in Halifax."<br>"This is the oldest building in Halifax," the guide told us. |

**A. Correct these sentences by adding commas in all the appropriate places.**

1. Our first performance will be on Friday December 10 2004 in the Betty Cadell Auditorium.

2. Joni Mitchell once said "I sing my sorrow and paint my joy."

3. If plane fares are too expensive why don't you take the bus?

4. I sometimes stay up to watch the late-night talk shows but the ones that are on in the daytime with their tell-all approach to people's problems appal me.

5. As we walked musicians serenaded us with jazz which they played on a range of instruments.

6. My father always said "Do your best and forget the rest."

7. You can leave my dear whenever you want but don't expect anyone to follow you.

8. The djellaba the long loose gown worn by men in Arabic countries is a sensible form of clothing in extremely hot climates.

9. I travelled to London England on Monday June 9 2003 for a conference.

10. Although I haven't spoken to Keosha my old neighbour in a long time I still think of her fondly.

> - Use commas to separate two or more adjectives that modify the same noun.
>   EXAMPLE: tough, reliable boots [tough and reliable both modify "boots"]
> - Sometimes, one of the adjectives modifies the adjective that follows, or the adjective and the noun together. In these cases, no comma is necessary.
>   EXAMPLE: a pair of tough winter boots [tough modifies "winter boots"]
> - To figure out if a comma is necessary, reword the adjectives as a "that" clause. If it sounds natural, then use a comma.
>   EXAMPLE: boots that are tough and reliable [sounds natural, so use a comma]
>   boots that are tough and winter [sounds unnatural, so no comma]

**B. Add commas where necessary in the following phrases.**

**1.** a cool calm exterior

**2.** a helpful well-respected student

**3.** a complete background check

**4.** a broken wooden railing

**5.** a heartwarming uplifting episode

**6.** a thick limestone wall

> - The following examples illustrate common misuses of commas. Proofread your writing to make sure you have avoided these errors.

| Do NOT use a comma | Examples |
|---|---|
| to separate a verb and a subject complement (see Lesson 13) | **Wrong:** The object of the game is, to win. <br> **Correct:** The object of the game is to win. |
| to separate two parts of a compound subject or predicate | **Wrong:** The plant supervisor, and the office manager showed us around. <br> **Correct:** The plant supervisor and the office manager showed us around. <br><br> **Wrong:** The plant supervisor showed us around, and explained how things work. <br> **Correct:** The plant supervisor showed us around and explained how things work. |
| to set off an indirect quotation | **Wrong:** The guide told us, that this is the oldest building in Halifax. <br> **Correct:** The guide told us that this is the oldest building in Halifax. |
| between parts of a simple date (month and year only) | **Wrong:** August, 2003 <br> **Correct:** August 2003 |

**C. Circle any unnecessary commas in the following sentences.**

**1.** Caitlin invited us in, and made sure we were, well fed, relaxed, and comfortable.

**2.** The owner of the car, and his parents, showed up at the trial, but they did not testify.

**3.** If you have a part-time job, you can't just decide to go camping, and forget to tell your supervisor.

**4.** The May/June, 2003, edition of *Moneytalk* magazine predicts that, mutual funds will rebound.

## Semicolons and Colons

A **semicolon** signals a more complete separation than a comma and a less complete separation than a period. Use a semicolon

- to separate items in a series if some of the items contain commas
    EXAMPLE:   The winners of the chess competition were Tanya Lobel,
              St. Stanislaus Collegiate; Mario Estevez, Harcourt Vocational
              Institute; and Marie Edwards, P.C. Cummings Collegiate.

- in place of a period to separate related sentences. Using a semicolon instead of a period emphasizes the connection between the two sentences.
    EXAMPLE:   Last summer's drought was disastrous for Western farmers;
              however, this year promises to be better.

A **colon** signals to the reader that what follows will in some way complete the idea in the preceding clause. Use a colon

- after an independent clause to introduce a list, a quotation, or an explanation
    EXAMPLES:   An astronaut must have three qualities: a cool head, an aptitude for
               science, and a positive attitude.
               Most episodes of *Made in Canada* end with the same statement:
               "I think that went well."
               All contestants will go home with a great prize: a pen that writes
               in blue and red ink.
    **No Colon Needed:** To be an astronaut, you must have a cool
               head, an aptitude for science, and a positive attitude.

- instead of a period or semicolon between two independent clauses. Choose a colon when you want to emphasize that the second clause summarizes or explains the first clause.
    EXAMPLE:   Mr. Bartok is a great teacher: he treats his students with respect
              and inspires them to do their best.

**Add semicolons or colons where necessary in the sentences that follow.**

1. I've just been reading about a famous scientist Gregor Mendel.

2. Mendel lived from 1822 to 1884 during his lifetime, he experimented on 20 000 plants.

3. Mendel's family was poor they struggled to put him through school.

4. Mendel's experiments began with a simple question "How do plants inherit different traits?"

5. Mendel used two kinds of peas round and wrinkled.

6. He noticed that when a plant with round peas was pollinated by a plant with wrinkled peas, the offspring was also round in fact, the only way to get a wrinkled offspring was to pollinate a wrinkled pea with pollen from another wrinkled pea.

7. Mendel concluded that the round trait was "dominant" it took precedence over the wrinkled trait.

8. Since then, many dominant genes have been identified in humans brown eyes and baldness, for example.

9. You can find out about Mendel's experiments in the following books *Gregor Mendel and Heredity* by Wilma George *Famous Men of Modern Biology* by Melvin Berger and *Mendel's Peas* by Anna Pavlicek.

10. Mendel received little recognition for his work during his lifetime it was not until the early twentieth century that he was recognized for what he was the father of modern genetics.

- Use **parentheses** to add non-essential information or asides, or in place of commas to set off non-restrictive elements. Parenthetical material is usually considered less important than material set off by commas or dashes.

  EXAMPLES: To no one's surprise, the publisher rejected the script right away (I doubt they even read past the title page).

  To no one's surprise (except perhaps the author's), the publisher rejected the script right away.

- Never use a comma, dash, colon, or semicolon before the opening parenthesis.

  EXAMPLE: **Wrong:** Whenever I fly, (which I do often), I get scared.

  **Correct:** Whenever I fly (which I do often), I get scared.

**A. Correct any errors in punctuation and use of parentheses in the following sentences.**

1. I left three messages on your voice mail (at least I think it was yours—but you never responded.

2. My old school—(Jamieson Elementary is holding a reunion next year.

3. My uncle tried skydiving on his fiftieth birthday, (He says it's never too late to learn).

4. I will have to buy a whole new wardrobe: (shoes, blouses, business suits, and a briefcase) if I get the job.

- A **dash** (—) or pair of dashes can be used in place of several other types of punctuation, as shown below.

| A dash can replace | Examples |
|---|---|
| **commas** to set off a non-restrictive element | The play—which closed yesterday—got poor reviews |
| a **colon** to introduce a list, quotation, or explanation | An astronaut must have three qualities—a cool head, an aptitude for science, and a positive attitude. <br> Most episodes of *Made in Canada* end with the same statement—"I think that went well." <br> All contestants will go home with a great prize— a pen that writes in blue and red ink. |
| a **semicolon** to separate closely related sentences | Last summer's drought was disastrous for farmers— however, this year has been better. |
| **parentheses** for asides and non-essential information | To no one's surprise, the publisher rejected the script right away—I doubt they even read past the title page. <br> To no one's surprise—except perhaps the author's— the publisher rejected the script right away. |

- To avoid overuse, restrict your use of dashes to situations that require a strong emphasis or that signal a sudden change of tone or thought.

**B. Use proofreader's marks in the following sentences to replace the dashes with other punctuation.**

1. It was the students—not the staff—who organized the whole event.

2. I was thrilled that I passed the test—it was the third time I had tried.

3. David Smythe—who was my Economics professor at university years ago—is now a millionaire.

4. Alan will only accept criticism from one person—his sister Monica.

5. It was the first warm day after a long, cold winter—and there I was stuck at home with the flu.

### Punctuating Quotations

- Use **quotation marks** to show the exact words of a speaker or source. Put **periods** and **commas** inside the quotation marks.

    EXAMPLES: "Expectations are everything."
    "Call me in the morning," the doctor said.

- Speech tags (he said, she said, etc.) can go before or after the quotation. They can also be placed in the middle of a quoted sentence. The quotation and the introductory words are usually separated by commas.

    EXAMPLES: **Before Quotation:** Jim said, "Let's go together."
    **After Quotation:** "Let's go together," said Jim.
    **Within Quotation:** "Let's go together," said Jim, "so no one gets lost."

- If the quoted material is incorporated into the sentence, no commas are needed.

    EXAMPLES: Her belief that "everything will be all right" is unrealistic.
    At the convention, delegates chanted slogans and waved placards that read "It's Our Turn" and "We're Number One!"

- When quoting from an original source, use a **colon** instead of a comma if an independent clause introduces the quotation, or if the quotation itself is more than one sentence long.

    EXAMPLES: Rule seventeen reads as follows: "No member shall bring a pet or other animal onto the premises without written consent."
    His statement read: "I appreciate the support of every member of my campaign team. Without your help, this victory would not have been possible."

**A. Add missing punctuation to the following sentences.**

1. In his tribute to Pierre Trudeau, Rex Murphy says___He bore a symbolic relationship with his time___

2. ___This report is incomplete___ Anna pointed out.

3. The best advice I ever got is this___Never complain; never explain___

4. This candidate claims in her cover letter that she is ___competent, confident, and ready to work___

5. The movie *Casablanca* ends with these famous lines___Major Strasser has been shot. Round up the usual suspects___

6. ___If you can't leave in a taxi___ says comedian Groucho Marx in the movie *Duck Soup*___you can leave in a huff. If that's too soon, you can leave in a minute and a huff___

7. The most famous line from *Monty Python's Flying Circus* is ___And now for something completely different___

8. We can and should read books___not to throw light on literature, not to become familiar with famous people, but to refresh and exercise our own creative powers___suggests Virginia Woolf.

9. Consider the words of Salman Rushdie___One of the things a writer is for is to say the unsayable, speak the unspeakable, and ask difficult questions___

10. Jane Goodall believes education is the key to conservation___Laws alone are useless. We already have animal-protection laws that mean nothing because they're not enforced—and they never will mean anything until we get to people's hearts___

- Put **semicolons** and **colons** outside the quotation marks, unless they are part of the original quotation.

  EXAMPLES:  Your letter states, "The faulty merchandise will be replaced immediately"; however, we have not yet received the replacement.
  Jared despairs of only one thing in "The Fool": unrequited love.

- Put **exclamation marks** and **question marks** outside the quotation marks, unless they are part of the original quotation.

  EXAMPLES:  The store's slogan is "Why Go Anywhere Else?"
  Isn't the other store's slogan "We Care"?
  Just before the rock slide, Rhonda screamed, "Look out!"
  It drives me crazy when people say, "Have a nice day"!

**B.  Add correct punctuation to the sentences that follow.**

   1. Interviewers often ask ____What can you offer this company____

   2. What is the point of saying____It can't be done____

   3. One reviewer called the play____a gem____another called it____a diamond in the rough____

   4. Only one player has ever earned the title____The Great One____Wayne Gretzky.

   5. Throughout the hockey game, a group of spectators kept chanting____Fight! Fight____

   6. I couldn't believe my ears when she said____We no longer require your services____

- Use **single quotation marks** for a quotation within a quotation. When single and double quotations are beside each other, leave a space between them.

  EXAMPLE:   "Look for a sign that reads 'No Left Turn,' " he said.

**C.  Add single and double quotation marks along with any necessary punctuation to the sentences that follow.**

   1. Lauren explained, ____The letter was addressed ____Dear Ms. James____

   2. ____My favourite poem in the anthology is ____Love Is Not All____ by Edna St. Vincent Millay____said Walter.

   3. The producer said____Stairway to Heaven____by Led Zeppelin is a rock classic____

- For longer quotations (four lines or more), or poetry excerpts of more than two lines, do not use quotation marks. Instead, begin the quotation on a new line, and set it off from the text by indenting ten spaces from the left margin. Include a sentence that introduces the quotation, followed by a colon.

  EXAMPLE:   T.S. Eliot's *Four Quartets* begins with a statement that sounds more like a philosophical argument than a poem:
  Time present and time past
  Are both perhaps present in time future,
  And time future contained in time past.
  If all time is eternally present
  All time is unredeemable.

**D.  Choose an excerpt of at least two lines from a poem you have studied this year. In your notebook, write an appropriate introductory sentence. Then, present the excerpt in the proper format and with correct punctuation.**

- Use three spaced dots, or **ellipses** (…), to indicate that material has been omitted from a quoted sentence. Note that in general, no ellipses are needed for omissions at the beginning of a quotation.

    EXAMPLE:    **Original:** Let me say that Robert De Niro is, in my humble opinion, one of the best actors of his generation.

    **Quotation:** One critic raved that "Robert De Niro is…one of the best actors of his generation."

- If the omission comes at the end of a sentence, a period follows the ellipses.

    EXAMPLE:    **Original:** Over the next two decades, the music video would impact every aspect of popular culture, influencing advertising, fashion, publishing, film, and television.    —"Video Ga Ga" by Vinay Menon

    **Quotation:** "Over the next two decades, the music video would impact every aspect of popular culture…."

**A. Refer to the original passage below to correct the quotations that follow. Use proofreader's marks to insert ellipses and quotation marks where necessary.**

It would be folly to attempt to sum up Purdy's poetic universe: like Walt Whitman's it's too vast for a précis. What interested him could be anything, but above all the wonder that anything at all can be interesting. He was always turning banality inside out. For me, he was, above all, an explorer—pushing into nameless areas of landscape, articulating the inarticulate, poking around in dusty corners of memory and discovering treasure there, digging up the bones and shards of a forgotten ancestral past. When he wasn't capering about and joking and scratching his head over the idiocy and pain and delight of being alive, he was composing lyric elegies for what was no longer alive, but had been—and, through his words, still is.

   —from "The Awkward Sublime" by Margaret Atwood

1. It would be folly to attempt to sum up Purdy's poetic universe.

2. For me, he was an explorer

3. When he wasn't scratching his head over the idiocy and pain and delight of being alive, he was

    composing lyric elegies for what was no longer alive

- Use **square brackets** when adding explanatory words that are not part of the original quotation. Also use square brackets if you have to change or replace a word in the original to make it fit your sentence, or if you change the capitalization of a word.

    EXAMPLE:    **Original:** Instead of letting countries treat it as a commonly held resource allocated for the general good, they want it considered as a commodity traded by private investors for profit.    —"Blue Gold" by Jim Hightower

    **Quotation:** Jim Hightower suggests that corporations are out to change the traditional view of water as a public resource: "[T]hey want it [water] considered as a commodity traded by private investors for profit."

**B. In your notebook, write two quotations based on the original passage in Part A. Your quotations should illustrate at least two different uses of square brackets.**

# Lesson 52

## Punctuating Titles

- Generally, use italics (or underlining if you're not using a computer) when referring to titles of complete works, and quotation marks when referring to the title of a work within a longer work.

| Italics or Underlining | | Quotation Marks | |
|---|---|---|---|
| **Books** | *Colony of Unrequited Dreams* by Wayne Johnston | **Book Chapters** | Chapter 2, "A Triumphant Return" |
| **Long Poems** | *The Wasteland* by T.S. Eliot | **Short Poems** | "Provisions" by Margaret Atwood |
| **Newspapers and Magazines** | *The Globe and Mail* *Chatelaine* | **Newspaper and Magazine Articles** | "Heroes and Holy Innocents" by Kathi Wolfe |
| **TV and Radio Programs** | *Disclosure* | **TV and Radio Episodes** | "Episode 8: The Discovery" |
| **Albums** | *Sea of No Cares* by Great Big Sea | **Song Titles** | "Yarmouth Town" by Great Big Sea |
| **Complete Plays** | *Galileo: The Starry Messenger* by Lindsay Price | **Short Stories** | "Things That Fly" by Douglas Coupland |
| **Films** | *Casablanca* | | |
| **Works of Art** | *Me and My Parrots* by Frida Kahlo | | |

**Add quotation marks and underlining where necessary in the following sentences.**

1. The films A Beautiful Mind and Girl, Interrupted both deal with mental illness.

2. The March 2, 2003, episode of the CBC TV series Venture was called H2: Powering the Future.

3. An interesting article called Reflections on Inuit Art, written by Betty Bell, appears in the book Inuit Art: An Anthology.

4. For tomorrow, please review Chapter 15, The Impressionists, in your textbook A History of Art.

5. Alberto Ruggieri's painting Man Looking at the Cosmos is used to illustrate Ethan Canin's short story Star Food.

6. The Collected Works of Billy the Kid is a long poem by Michael Ondaatje that explores the life of the famous outlaw.

7. Some of Ondaatje's shorter poems, such as A House Divided, appeared in his poetry collection The Cinnamon Peeler.

8. I read a review of a production of Tennessee Williams' play The Glass Menagerie in Maclean's last Friday.

9. The TV show Made in Canada used the Tragically Hip song Blow at High Dough, from their album Up to Here, as its theme song.

10. The National Post had a feature on Barbara Gowdy's book The Romantic.

- Use apostrophes to form singular and plural possessive nouns.
  - EXAMPLES: Gabrielle's pencil          the servants' quarters
- If a noun ends in an s or z sound, and adding an -s to form the possessive will make it difficult to pronounce, you may add just an apostrophe.
  - EXAMPLE: Jack Jones's cat          OR          Jack Jones' cat
- Use apostrophes to show that letters or numbers have been omitted. (Note that till meaning "until," though, and round do not require apostrophes, but 'til does.)
  - EXAMPLES: don't     the class of '05     What are you doin'?
- Some writers use an apostrophe to show the plural of letters, or of words used as words. Others do not. Whichever style you use, apply it consistently.
  - EXAMPLES: mind your p's and q's     the aye's have it (OR "the ayes have it")
- Use apostrophes in time expressions such as those that follow.
  - EXAMPLES: one month's time          two hours' drive

**A. Add apostrophes where necessary in the following sentences.**

1. Hows it goin ol pal?

2. The Wilsons family tree has several Arthurs in it.

3. Heres a 98 Mazda for sale, though whos to say if its in good shape.

4. Candaces arms in a sling cause she broke it.

5. Ms. Hodgkins cousins live a few minutes walk from Sarahs house.

---

- Using too many apostrophes is a common error. Remember that plural words do not require an apostrophe unless they are also possessive. Also remember that the possessive pronoun its does not require an apostrophe.
  - EXAMPLES: **Incorrect:** The queen of spade's is missing from this deck.
    **Correct:** The queen of spades is missing from this deck.

    **Incorrect:** Why does this dog bite it's own tail?
    **Correct:** Why does this dog bite its own tail?

**B. Use proofreader's marks to eliminate unnecessary apostrophes and correct misplaced ones. Then, make any other necessary changes to ensure the sentences are correct.**

1. When it's warm, there'll be bunch's of grape's on those vine's.

2. The coffee shop around the corner's the place where the student's hang out.

3. The Jameses' live a few minute's from here.

4. Richard's cousin ordered two cola's and offered one to Dion Jones'.

5. Navjeet prefer's the caffe latte's at this cafe to the one's at the other coffee shop.

6. Joes' competing in several category's during this years' swim meet.

7. Todays' paper arrived late because the delivery persons' van broke down.

8. Were using Reyam's computer because our's has crashed.

9. That entertainment centres' expensive; it's going to cost me at least two month's wage's.

10. Evas' friend's coming to visit her.

A **hyphen** is used to join parts of a word or phrase. Since hyphen use in compound words changes over time, it is advisable to check a dictionary. In general, use a hyphen in the following situations:

- in compound adjectives before a noun, BUT not when the same words follow the noun. A **compound adjective** is two or more words that function as a single adjective.

  EXAMPLES: a <u>three-metre</u> drop   BUT   a drop of three metres
  
  a <u>hard-to-find</u> recording   BUT   a recording that is hard to find
  
  a <u>sixteen-year-old</u> student   BUT   a student who is sixteen years old

- in some compound nouns and verbs. Check a dictionary, as hyphen use in compound nouns and verbs changes over time.

  EXAMPLES: shut-in   double-check   hand-me-down

- after the prefixes all- and self-, and after other prefixes if omitting the hyphen might cause confusion or misreading

  EXAMPLES: self-basting   all-knowing   re-enter   co-exist

- for written fractions and compound numbers from twenty-one to ninety-nine

  EXAMPLES: one-third   twenty-two   one hundred and seventy-six

- Do **not** use a hyphen between an adverb ending in -ly and an adjective; in this case, there is no confusion about the function of the words.

  EXAMPLES: a newly admitted patient   a hastily prepared meal

**A. Use proofreader's marks to insert hyphens where needed in the following sentences. Consult a dictionary as necessary.**

1. Please double check your well to ensure it is at least seven and a half metres deep.

2. We rented an air conditioned suite in a well known hotel.

3. Michael's self satisfied expression gave me an all consuming desire to get even!

4. A hastily assembled group of well wishers were on hand to hear a long winded speech marking the launch of a preeminent new cooperative venture.

---

- Use a hyphen to divide a word at the end of a line. Divide words between syllables, and avoid leaving a syllable of two letters or less on a line. Do not hyphenate one-syllable words or proper nouns.

  EXAMPLES: rein-force   div-ision   inabil-ity

---

**B. Indicate where you would hyphenate these words if they appeared at the end of a line. Check a dictionary, if necessary. If the word should not be hyphenated, circle it.**

1. impartial _____      4. dismantled _____

2. sprouted _____      5. carrier _____

3. execute _____      6. Macdonald _____

**A. Add commas to the following sentences.**

1. A little voice inside my head said "Don't do it!"

2. Tuesday October 15 2002 was the last time we met.

3. According to this pamphlet Paris France is the most popular tourist destination in the world.

4. It was a long hard haul up the last hill and when we arrived we were all exhausted.

5. Since we don't have cilantro dill or thyme we can't use this recipe.

**B. Remove unnecessary commas from the following sentences.**

1. The soft, soothing, classical, music soothed our nerves, and calmed everybody down.

2. Unfortunately, the woman who gave us the tour, and my companion Danica, did not get along.

3. The client claims, that she paid $400 in January, 2003.

4. The trouble with using an overcomplicated, garbage-sorting, system like this one is, no one will bother.

5. Curtis exclaimed, "I've been late every day, since my watch broke, so I'm going to buy a new one!"

**C. Add semicolons and colons in the following sentences.**

1. The procedure to follow in an emergency is as follows (1) at the sound of the alarm, line up in pairs (2) leave the building by the nearest exit (3) meet at the prearranged meeting place (4) do a head count.

2. I'm afraid to visit that amusement park it was closed by safety inspectors twice last year.

3. John Franklin is considered the greatest Arctic explorer however, even he did not succeed in finding the Northwest Passage.

4. I found the perfect play for the drama club's next performance *The Odd Couple*.

5. Author Annie Dillard has a unique perspective on writing "Fiction keeps its audience by retaining the world as its subject matter."

**D. Add dashes and hyphens to each sentence, where appropriate.**

1. The boss took a hard line approach she insisted that we arrive on time for every shift.

2. Dennis compiled an all inclusive list of the entire crew the only person he forgot to include was himself.

3. Cooperation between the marketing and production departments is crucial to a successful product launch especially in this case.

4. The lawyer withheld twenty five percent of the settlement that's one quarter of the total as payment for legal fees and expenses.

5. The court order which a sheriff hand delivered to her last known address orders her to appear in court next week.

6. This report is a real eye opener it shows that many school drop outs may end up in low paying jobs.

E. **For the first FOUR sentences in Part D, indicate another appropriate form of punctuation that could replace the dashes. (You don't have to rewrite the sentence; just record the alternative.) Use a different form of punctuation for each sentence.**

1. _____     3. _____

2. _____     4. _____

F. **Add underlining and quotation marks where necessary in the following sentences.**

1. The headline in the Vancouver Sun screamed Peace Breaks Out!

2. A writer at Rolling Stone magazine gave Michael Moore's film Bowling for Columbine an excellent review.

3. Shirley Jackson's classic short story The Lottery sends shivers down my spine every time I read it.

4. In the sixties, the song We Shall Overcome became a rallying cry for the Civil Rights Movement.

5. If you liked Carol Shields' novel Unless, you might want to see a production of her play Thirteen Hands.

G. **Add quotation marks and other punctuation to the following quotations.**

1. A poster in the Guidance department read Do You Know Where You're Headed

2. When Dora saw the cat, she exclaimed What a terrible mess you are

3. I just can't believe that this dump was advertised as a luxury resort

4. Have you read that article titled The Future of Hunger

5. Whatever you do said Sean don't forget to water those plants

6. Andrea gave Milo a choice Either meet me at my house and we'll walk over together, or drop by the gym later on

7. We can all expect to pay more at the gas pumps warned the analyst.

8. I'm not sure what she meant when she called me a bright light without an off-switch moreover, I'm not anxious to find out!

H. **Use proofreader's marks to add ellipses and square brackets where necessary to the following quotations. Refer to the original quotation in the box for guidance.**

> The Canadian people have had enough. They recognize that this government, Mr. Speaker, is not giving them the information they need to make an informed decision in the upcoming referendum. It has consistently refused to release documents that I believe have a direct bearing on the issue, and which could influence the way people vote.

1. One opposition MP complained about the government's lack of openness with regard to the referendum: "This government is not giving them the Canadian public the information they need to make an informed decision."

2. The MP accused the government of "consistently refusing to release documents that have a direct bearing on the issue, and which could influence the way people vote."

**Follow the steps below to correct this passage.**

Spam used to be, a luncheon meat. Now, its a fact of life for anyone who uses e-mail—in other word's, the vast majority of Canadians. Spam refers to unsolicited mail promoting mostly-useless products and scheme's that promise to make you: rich, happy, thin, healthy, or whatever—but mostly rich. Many of them have subject lines like: Miracle Drug Cures All Diseases;" others proclaim that you can "Earn $40 000 in Three Weeks!!!".

Of course, not many people, actually believe these marketers claims. On the other hand, it doesn't take a lot of believer's to make e-mail a money making vehicle for spammer's—John Mozena of the Coalition Against Unsolicited Commercial E-mail claims that, even a one in a million response rate can generate a profit. Thats because, the cost of sending one e-mail is the same as the cost of sending one-million. With such a large sample, a marketers bound to find at least one victim—perhaps a child or some very trusting soul—whos naive enough to hand over his or her money.

And now, an article that appeared in "The Globe and Mail" in April, 2001, (Cell Phone Users Slam Wireless Spam" reports, some people have started receiving spam via their phones text-messaging service. Since the cost of retrieving these messages, ends up on the users bill at months end this type of spam is particularly annoying.

A.  **Find 17 unnecessary punctuation marks and remove them.**

B.  **Find 16 punctuation marks that are missing and insert them.**

C.  **Find 2 punctuation marks that are used incorrectly and replace them with another more suitable form of punctuation.**

D.  **Identify another form of punctuation that could replace each use of dashes in the excerpt; then, decide whether the dash or the alternative punctuation is more appropriate in each case. Give a reason for your answer.**

   **1.** Alternative punctuation: _____

      Assessment: _____

   **2.** Alternative punctuation: _____

      Assessment: _____

   **3.** Alternative punctuation: _____

      Assessment: _____

   **4.** Alternative punctuation: _____

      Assessment: _____

**E.** Choose an extract that is at least four lines long from the paragraphs on the previous page. Write an introductory sentence for the quotation, using correct punctuation. Then, insert the quotation below, using the correct form for long quotations.

_____

_____

_____

_____

_____

**F.** Add correct punctuation to the quotations below. Check the quotations against the original passage in the box. Then, use proofreader's marks to insert square brackets indicating changes and explanatory words, and ellipses indicating omissions.

> According to most experts, there's only one sure-fire way to get rid of spam—stop using the Internet. That said, you _can_ reduce the amount of unsolicited e-mail you receive. First, never respond to spam, even if the message has an address you can write to in order to have yourself "unsubscribed" or "deleted." Many companies use these "unsubscribe" or "delete" responses as proof that your address is still in use. As a result, instead of receiving fewer unsolicited e-mails, you will probably receive even more than before. Some e-mail programs allow you to filter out spam by blocking certain addresses. However, there will always be new sources of spam—you can't block them all. A third option (if you're willing to pay) is to install an anti-spam filter on your computer. These filters won't catch every unwanted piece of mail—but they will certainly reduce the number significantly.

1. How can you reduce the amount of unsolicited e-mail you receive? One writer suggests Never respond to spam, even if the message has an address you can write to in order to have yourself unsubscribed or deleted

2. The writer explains that many companies use these responses as proof that your address is still in use

3. It is really shocking that asking to be deleted from marketers' lists means you will probably receive even more unsolicited e-mails than before!

4. Do you think the writer was serious when she suggested that the only way to eliminate spam is to stop using the Internet

5. The article claims that using your e-mail program to block messages is not effective There will always be new sources of spam—you can't block them all; however, I have had good results with this method.

## Purpose and Audience

> ■ The **purpose** of a piece of writing is the effect the writer hopes to achieve. Some common purposes for writing include to inform, to persuade, and to entertain. Although more than one of these goals may be achieved in a single piece of writing, one purpose usually predominates.

**A. Each of the following passages describes the same incident—the attempted raising of the hull section of the H.M.S. *Titanic*. In your notebook, identify the main purpose of each passage. Then, give three examples of how the purpose affects the language, tone, and content of each passage.**

1. In the summer of 1996, a company called RMS Titanic, Inc. attempted to lift a 7000-ton hull piece from the wreck of the *Titanic*. An audience of 1600 people gathered to witness the event. The attempt was part of an ongoing salvage operation that has seen many artifacts from the wreck brought up from the ocean floor. The plan was to float the hull section by attaching it to a series of ropes tied to balloons filled with diesel fuel. Since diesel is lighter than water, it was expected that the hull would slowly float upward to the surface, more than 3 kilometres overhead. However, the salvage was thwarted by the powerful currents and strong winds of Hurricane Edward, which was building in the region. The lines became tangled, and one by one, the ropes broke. When it was approximately 60 metres from the surface, the hull slipped free and sank back to the ocean bed. It landed 10 kilometres away from its original location.

2. The elite audience waited excitedly as the hull piece, 3000 metres beneath the waves, was slowly lifted toward the surface on ropes. But the captain of the ship was looking worried. Winds were picking up, and the water was churning violently. News that a hurricane was in the area did nothing to calm the crew's jitters. Would the operation be completed in time? They were so close…. Then, disaster struck. Pulled by the fierce currents, first one, then another of the ropes broke. The last rope let go when the wreckage was just 60 metres from the surface. The hull piece slid silent as a tomb back down to its resting place at the bottom of the sea. The fickle ocean had won yet again.

3. It's hard to believe that anyone would be willing to pay $7000 to watch a graveyard be destroyed. Yet that is just what happened in 1996, when over 1600 gawkers paid to watch the raising of a part of the *Titanic*. Thousands of men, women, and children went to their deaths in that ship. Disturbing the wreckage means disturbing their final resting place. To make the event even more ghoulish, the curious crowd were treated to a replica of the last meal served on board the ship on the night it went down. However, perhaps fate intervened to thwart the plan. During the attempt to lift the hull, high winds and powerful currents broke the ropes. Before it could be hauled to the surface, the hull sank back down to its rightful place at the sea bottom. May it rest in peace.

> ■ The **audience** is the person or persons for whom you are writing. Characteristics of audiences that are of particular interest to writers include their age, interests, attitudes, and level of knowledge or expertise. For example, the writer of the first paragraph in Part A assumes that the audience has some general knowledge about the *Titanic*, but no technical expertise about salvage operations.

**B. In your notebook, list three ways that the informative passage in Part A might be different if it were part of a report addressed to marine salvage specialists.**

**C. In your notebook, list three ways the persuasive passage in Part A might differ if it were written for an audience of business executives interested in investing in RMS Titanic, Inc.**

# Lesson
# 56

## Formal and Informal Writing

- The degree of formality you use in writing depends on your purpose and audience. However, always maintain a consistent level of formality within the same piece.

| **Formal**<br>(used for academic essays, reports, business letters, and official documents) | **Informal**<br>(used for personal letters, dialogue, and sometimes for articles in magazines) |
|---|---|
| usually written in third person (it, one, he, she) with few or no personal references to audience or writer | usually written in first or second person (I, we, you) |
| uses standard English (see Lesson 4); avoids colloquialisms or slang; may use specialized vocabulary | uses colloquial expressions and a conversational level of vocabulary; may include slang expressions or dialect |
| often has a smooth, regular rhythm, with a balanced variety of sentence structures and lengths | rhythm imitates casual speech; sentences tend to be shorter and simpler |
| carefully observes the conventions of grammar and punctuation, and avoids sentence fragments, contractions, and abbreviations | sometimes breaks conventions to imitate conversational English; frequently uses fragments, contractions, and abbreviations |

**A. Underline examples in the passage below that illustrate each of the <u>informal</u> writing characteristics listed in the chart above.**

Shakespeare's all the rage. You'll find his fingerprints all over pop culture and show biz. He's quoted more often than any other author. And he's inspired more than 350 movies. In 2000, he was voted "Artist of the Millennium." Not bad for a guy who's been dead for almost 400 years.

How come we're not all sick of him? Well, for one thing, his characters are like real people, with real problems. Think about it. Most of us don't live in a Danish castle like Hamlet. But at one time or another we've all found it tough to do the right thing. And I guess anyone who fell in love in high school, and then got flak from the parents, can relate to *Romeo and Juliet*.

**B. Using the list of <u>formal</u> writing characteristics in the chart, make ten revisions to the following paragraph to make it more formal. Use proofreader's marks.**

In my opinion, it's the vividness of Shakespeare's characters and his profound understanding of human nature that explain why his works have been reconfigured in so many different settings. I mean, ever since the 1960s musical *West Side Story* transplanted Romeo and Juliet onto the gang-controlled streets of NY, myriads of clever Shakespeare productions have appeared on film. For example, the movie *O*, which is a cinematic version of *Othello*, set on a basketball court. In director Michael Almereyda's take on *Hamlet*, a young filmmaker, played by Ethan Hawke, agonizes over the death of his father, the CEO of the Denmark Corporation. And in *Romeo Must Die*, we see Jet Li transform the "star-crossed lover" into a violent action hero. Even Shakespeare's more difficult plays—those that portray a world view or morality that doesn't jive with today's mores—have found their way into the theatres in modernized versions. The '99 flick *Ten Things I Hate About You* converts the anti-feminist play *The Taming of the Shrew* into a romantic comedy set in an American high school.

## Patterns of Development

Essays and other kinds of writing can be organized in various ways, depending on the subject matter, the purpose, and the intended audience. The following patterns can be used to organize a single paragraph or a whole essay:

- chronological or time sequence (e.g., narratives and factual accounts)
- spatial or location order (e.g., descriptions)
- by feature or characteristic (e.g., comparisons, descriptions)
- by relevance or importance (e.g., persuasive or business writing, news stories)
- cause–effect sequence (e.g., science reports, explanations, instructions)
- by logic or reasoning (e.g., arguments, analyses)

**A.  Identify the pattern of development in each of the following paragraphs.**

1. For most people, the most compelling reason for using public transit is cost. It has been estimated that running a car costs on average about $5000 to $6000 a year. A transit pass costs just a fraction of that. Not only will using the bus and subway save you money, they are also a great way to get some "down time"; a half-hour bus ride is like an enforced rest in the midst of our hectic lives. And then, of course, there's the environmental argument. Instead of sitting in your gas-guzzling car, stuck in traffic, you can congratulate yourself for using a much more "green" form of transportation.

    Pattern: _____

2. Increasing service levels is the best way to reverse the declining ridership trends for public transportation. By setting aside dedicated lanes for buses and by running subways more frequently, we create the perception that public transit is an efficient way to travel. This perception will, in turn, lead to increased ridership, which will boost our revenues. We estimate that the revenue increase will, over ten years, more than pay for the initial expense of service improvements.

    Pattern: _____

- Each paragraph or section of an essay or research paper also has a pattern of development. For example, a paper examining the history of aviation in Canada might include a section on the early bush pilots that is arranged by example or by feature, while the paper as a whole is arranged chronologically. Headings often provide clues to the overall pattern of development.

**B.  Suggest an appropriate pattern of development for each section of the outline below. The topic is the United Nations.**

Outline Topic                                          Pattern of Development

I.  The Founding of the UN                    _____

II.  The Original Mandate of the UN        _____

III. Some Recent UN Success Stories        _____

IV. Kosovo: Why the UN Failed to Act      _____

V.  The Future: Four Proposals for Change  _____

Overall Pattern: _____

# Lesson 58

## Formulating a Thesis

- A **thesis** is a statement of the main idea of an essay or paper. It proposes an opinion that the rest of the paper proves. In school essays and other academic work, the thesis is usually stated in the opening paragraph, and the topic sentence of each paragraph that follows expands upon or supports the thesis.

- A thesis should be broad enough to include all the subtopics, information, or arguments presented in the essay. Statistics and other narrow statements of fact do not allow enough scope for opinion.

  EXAMPLE:  **Too Narrow:** Canada has participated in over seventy peacekeeping operations overseas.

- However, a thesis should also be narrow enough to enable you to cover it thoroughly in the space available. That is why you should avoid using extreme words such as <u>all</u>, <u>never</u>, or <u>always</u> in your thesis. Such statements are hard to back up.

  EXAMPLES:  **Too Broad:** Canadian Peacekeepers are the best in the world.
  **Focused:** The Canadian Armed Forces have developed a reputation for courage and compassion, as their role in three recent world conflicts demonstrates.

---

**A.  For each topic, underline the sentence that would make the <u>best</u> thesis for a short essay.**

1. Topic: Naturalized Lawns
   (a) A naturalized lawn is easier to maintain and better for the environment than the traditional grass lawn.
   (b) A naturalized lawn is the only rational approach to lawn care.
   (c) Naturalized lawns are lawns with vegetation that requires little maintenance.

2. Topic: Garbage Incineration
   (a) Many communities still rely on incineration to deal with their garbage.
   (b) Incineration of garbage is never a good idea.
   (c) Incineration is not the definitive solution to the garbage problem, but it may have a role to play in helping us deal with our waste.

3. Topic: Starting a Summer Business
   (a) One great way to guarantee yourself a summer job is to start your own business.
   (b) Running your own summer business requires hard work, but it will give you great experience and a guaranteed summer job.
   (c) Last year, the government helped a record number of students start their own businesses.

4. Topic: Oscar Peterson
   (a) Oscar Peterson is arguably among the greatest jazz musicians Canada has ever produced.
   (b) Oscar Peterson was born in a modest home in Montréal.
   (c) Oscar Peterson believes that, "Regardless of it having been weakened by other forms of so-called music on the airways…somehow Jazz will maintain its creative place in the history of music of our world and time."

5. Topic: *The Charter of Rights and Freedoms*
   (a) We tend to forget that the Charter is not just a list of rights; it also sets out our responsibilities as citizens.
   (b) The Charter came into effect in 1982, as part of the repatriated Canadian Constitution.
   (c) The Charter has changed every aspect of life in Canada.

**B. Suggest a thesis sentence that expresses the main idea behind each group of sentences.**

1. Topic Sentence 1: Increasing tuition fees any further may force some students out of school.

   Topic Sentence 2: Lower enrolment will ultimately mean less revenue for colleges and universities.

   Topic Sentence 3: These lower revenues will lead to lower standards for admission.

   Topic Sentence 4: As our institutes of higher learning deteriorate, the best and the brightest will go elsewhere for their education.

   Thesis: _____

2. Topic Sentence 1: The first rule of motorcycle safety is to ensure your equipment is in good working order.

   Topic Sentence 2: Another important precaution is wearing proper protective gear.

   Topic Sentence 3: A safe motorcyclist positions the vehicle on the road for visibility and safety.

   Topic Sentence 4: Finally, you must learn to continually watch for and assess potential hazards on the road.

   Thesis: _____

3. Topic Sentence 1: Italian Fascism and German Nazism both arose in reaction to similar social conditions in Postwar Europe.

   Topic Sentence 2: While both Mussolini's Fascism and Hitler's Nazism had a broad base of popular support, Mussolini had less support from the working classes than Hitler did.

   Topic Sentence 3: Both the Fascists and the Nazis were characterized by an aggressive patriotism, but Mussolini's brand of nationalism was not as extreme as Hitler's.

   Thesis: _____

**C. Choose two topics from the list below and write a thesis statement for a short essay on each.**

- **how to look for a summer job or a university/college**
- **a comparison of two sports/novels/TV shows/films**
- **the importance of family/friendship/volunteering/voting**

1. Topic: _____

   Thesis: _____

   _____

   _____

2. Topic: _____

   Thesis: _____

   _____

   _____

# Lesson
## 59 Creating Unity

- Writing is unified if every sentence is related to a main idea. To create **unity** in an essay, you need to ensure everything you write supports your thesis. Each paragraph should contain a **topic sentence** that relates back to the thesis. The topic sentence is *usually* found near the beginning of the paragraph. The rest of the paragraph should contain facts, examples, or reasons that support the topic sentence.
- While experienced writers do not always state the topic sentence explicitly, when writing a school or academic essay it is best to include clear topic sentences in each paragraph.

**A. Underline the topic sentence in each paragraph. Then, improve the unity of the writing by crossing out sentences that are not closely connected to the topic sentence and thesis.**

**Thesis:** Advances in technology and changes in societal attitudes toward disability have led to a noticeable improvement in the quality of life for many individuals.

The most dramatic of these improvements so far have come from the widespread availability of computers. Computers have changed the way everyone lives and works, but they have had an even greater impact on people with disabilities. For instance, voice recognition software and "talking" computers now let people with little or no vision use computers. Those with physical disabilities can touch symbols or letters right on the screen, using a stick or other implement. Blissymbolics was invented by a Canadian. These and other innovations not only let users communicate with others much more easily, but they also allow them to continue their education through online and distance-learning courses.

In addition, new technologies to help people see, hear, walk, or talk are constantly appearing on the market. Experiments are now underway on digital implants that will actually help blind people to see by stimulating the optic nerve. Many people who are legally blind actually have some sight. Similarly, scientists are working on devices that may help people with paralysed limbs to control their movement through thought impulses, relayed by a small computer.

While there is still a long way to go to remove all the barriers, some change is apparent in attitudes toward disabilities as well. Thanks to a concerted publicity and outreach effort over the last twenty years, the public is much better informed about disability issues. Many organizations, such as the Canadian National Institute for the Blind, have been helping people with disabilities to adapt and function in day-to-day life for decades. In many schools, children with special needs are now integrated into regular classrooms. This integration has fostered greater understanding of disability, and with understanding comes a reduction in fear.

Employment equity programs by governments and private-sector companies have also opened doors for many Canadians with disabilities. As a result, unemployment among this segment of society has gone from about eighty percent just ten years ago, to about fifty percent today. Employment equity has also helped to increase job opportunities for Aboriginal people, visible minorities, and women. Clearly, there is still work to be done in this area; however, progress has been and is being made.

**B. Refer to the passage in Part A. Decide which kind of supporting detail—facts, examples, or reasons—is primarily used to support the topic sentence in each of the four paragraphs. Write your answers in your notebook.**

## Creating Coherence

Writing is **coherent** if sentences and paragraphs are clearly and smoothly connected. Writing that is not coherent is difficult to understand.

> EXAMPLE: **Not Coherent:** Writing, like any artform, requires creativity. We have to let our ideas flow freely, without censorship. Discovering what we have to say is the challenge. We are compelled to take risks. Many people find it hard to be creative. An internal editor constantly rejects imperfect or incomplete ideas that emerge.

The following techniques can improve the coherence of your writing.

- Use transition words, such as <u>furthermore</u>, <u>similarly</u>, <u>finally</u>, <u>however</u>, <u>consequently</u>, <u>for example</u>, <u>after</u>, and <u>since</u>. In the example below, note the use of <u>however</u> and <u>because</u>.
- Use a pronoun to refer back to a previous word or idea. In the example below, note the use of the pronouns <u>it</u> and <u>that</u>, as well as the consistent use of the third person (<u>we</u>, <u>us</u>, <u>our</u>).
- Repeat a key word from a previous sentence or paragraph. You can also choose a synonym for variety. In the passage, the words "creative" and "creatively" are repeated.
- Use parallel structure (see Lesson 46) to connect ideas of equal importance. For instance, "It challenges us…" and "It compels us…" are linked through parallel structure.

> EXAMPLE: **Coherent:** Writing, like any artform, requires creativity. The <u>creative</u> process involves letting our ideas flow freely, without censorship. <u>It challenges us</u> to dig deep to discover what we have to say. <u>It compels us</u> to take risks. <u>However</u>, many of us find it hard to express ourselves <u>creatively</u>. <u>That's because</u> <u>our</u> internal editor rejects the often imperfect or incomplete ideas that emerge from our creative self.

**In your notebook, identify as many examples as you can find in the following paragraphs of the four techniques for creating coherence.**

Freewriting is a technique often used by writers to silence their internal critic and encourage their creativity. This method is simple, yet effective. First, get a timer or clock and set it for ten minutes. Then, sit down and write without stopping until the buzzer goes off. Write without worrying about what you say, whether you are on topic, or how good your grammar is. If you get stuck, write the same thing over and over until you get started again. Often, the results of this exercise are surprising. For example, in the midst of the creative flow you may find interesting images or a new approach that you had not considered before.

However, the writing process entails more than just expressing your creative side. Any serious writer will tell you that after creativity comes the hard part—revision. Revision is what makes your work focused and organized. It is what brings clarity and wholeness to the often jumbled outpourings of the creative self. So, although the process of cutting away the "dead wood," the inappropriate images, and the rambling asides is less glamorous than the creative process that precedes it, it is just as important.

- In addition to presenting the thesis, the **introduction** of an essay, article, or report should grab the reader's interest and set the tone for the text that follows. Some techniques for creating interest include
  - telling an anecdote
  - describing a scene
  - presenting an interesting fact or statistic
  - posing a question
  - quoting from a reliable source
  - linking the topic to the experiences of the intended audience
- The following example uses a quotation as a way of introducing an essay:

  EXAMPLE: "An island," writes literary critic H.C. Goddard, "is a bit of a higher element rising out of a lower—a fragment of consciousness thrusting out of the ocean of unconsciousness." If this is true, then perhaps one way to interpret Shakespeare's *The Tempest*, which takes place on an island, is as a psychological drama. From this perspective, Caliban, Ariel, and Prospero could all be seen as aspects of the mind—what Freud would later call the Id, Ego, and Superego.

A. **Write an introduction for the article in Lesson 59. Decide on an appropriate technique for creating interest and use the following as your thesis: "Advances in technology and changes in societal attitudes toward disability have led to a noticeable improvement in the quality of life for many individuals."**

_____

_____

_____

_____

_____

_____

B. **Using one of the methods listed above, write an introduction for an essay on the topic, "Why the beaver is a good symbol for Canada."**

_____

_____

_____

_____

_____

> - The **conclusion** of an essay, article, or report summarizes or reinforces the main argument that has been presented. The conclusion may also refer back to an image or idea that was used in the introduction, and in some cases, may include a call to action. The following conclusion summarizes the main idea of the essay, and refers back to the quotation used in the introduction (see the box on the previous page).
>
>   EXAMPLE:   Shakespeare had been dead for almost 300 years when Freud was developing his theories about the subconscious. Yet, as we have seen, what is played out on Shakespeare's "fragment of consciousness" bears a remarkable similarity to the drama that Freud believed took place in every human psyche. Perhaps, in the end, this similarity reveals the convergence of two great minds, both with a profound insight into human nature.
>
> - The conclusion should not introduce new information or ideas that have not already been discussed in the body.

**C.** **Write a conclusion for the article in Lesson 59.**

_____

_____

_____

_____

_____

_____

_____

_____

**D.** **Review two essays you have written this term. Evaluate the introduction and conclusion of both papers, using the criteria in this lesson. In general, how might you improve on these parts of your writing?**

_____

_____

_____

_____

_____

_____

# Persuasive and Argumentative Writing

- **Argumentative writing** tries to convince the reader to accept an opinion or point of view. Most academic papers are argumentative. **Persuasive writing** goes further, and tries to push the reader to action or commitment.

- Effective persuasive or argumentative writing depends on a combination of reasoned arguments and emotional appeals. Persuasive writing is more likely to emphasize emotional appeals than argumentative writing.

- **Reasoned arguments** are those that are supported by facts, examples, or logic.

  EXAMPLE:   Beavers are not an appropriate symbol for Canada, because their dams have been known to cause destructive floods. If we consider ourselves environmentally responsible, we should choose a more appropriate animal as our symbol.

- **Emotional appeals** include using words with strong positive or negative connotations, evoking strong images through description or comparison, and appealing to universally accepted values.

  EXAMPLE:   The beaver is <u>nothing</u> but a large, furry rodent. Is this really the right creature to represent a <u>great</u> country like Canada? Are we a nation of <u>vermin</u>, or do we stand for something more <u>noble</u> than that?

- You can strengthen your argument by directly addressing any major arguments that might be raised against it, and successfully refuting them.

  EXAMPLE:   It's true that the beaver was once an important commodity, but a nation should be represented by something more than economics.

**A.   Read the passage below. Then, in your notebook, answer the questions that follow.**

The beaver may not be as glamorous as the bald-headed eagle, but it is nevertheless a fitting symbol of this country. For years, the fur trade played a significant role in establishing Canada's economy. In the eighteenth century, beaver pelts were the most precious commodity this country had to offer. It is only fair that the animal that allowed us to grow as a nation—at the cost of its own near extinction—should stand as the symbol of our country.

Besides, the beaver embodies many of the traits that we, as Canadians, value. The beaver lodge is a miracle of engineering. To build it, the beaver uses the abundant resources that are such an important part of this country to create a place of safety—much as the Aboriginal peoples who founded this land and learned to live in harmony with its natural wonders. The beaver is well known for its industry, and therefore, a fitting reminder of the hard work of the settlers who have also made their home here. And just as Canadians today pride themselves on their ability to adapt and compromise, so the beaver is at home both on land and in the water.

Ingenuity, hard work, and adaptability—the beaver stands for all these values. Canadians should be proud to display the beaver as the emblem of their nation.

1. Identify the two main arguments made in favour of the beaver as Canada's national symbol.

2. Identify one argument against the beaver that the author has anticipated.

3. Identify two examples of emotional appeals in the passage.

4. Suggest one change that you might make in order to strengthen the emotional appeal of the argument.

- Arrange the arguments in your thesis for maximum effectiveness. Remember that the beginning and the end of your essay have the strongest impact on your reader.
- If the audience you are writing for is sympathetic to your point of view, begin with your weaker arguments and build up to a strong conclusion. This arrangement leaves the reader with a good impression.
- If your audience is likely to be neutral or actively hostile to your ideas, you may prefer to begin with a strong argument in order to get the reader on side. You can then put your weaker arguments in the middle of the paper, and finish with another strong point.

B. **Assess the strength of the arguments for and against government-run lotteries given in the excerpts from a letter to the editor below. Rate them from 1 (strongest) to 4 (weakest).**

| Strength Assessment | Arguments For Government-Run Lotteries |
|---|---|
| | Government-run lotteries are an excellent source of revenue for the government. Most governments keep surprisingly little for themselves; most of the money, after the pay-out to winners, goes directly to charities and social agencies for the good of the whole community. |
| | Lotteries sell hope, which has a positive effect on people's well-being. There is nothing wrong with giving people a cheap, easy, and fun way to dream. We all need this kind of outlet. |
| | Only a small percentage of the population is addicted to gambling; the contribution made by lotteries to the well-being of society far outweighs the risk to a small portion of the population. Besides, if lotteries were not available, gamblers would still find any number of ways to feed their addiction. |
| | Lotteries are an alternative to taxes. They perform the same necessary function, but most people would far prefer to contribute voluntarily than to have the requirement to pay imposed from above. |

| Strength Assessment | Arguments Against Government-Run Lotteries |
|---|---|
| | Lotteries are a tax on the poor. Some studies show that people with low incomes spend proportionally more on lotteries than do those with higher incomes. This should not surprise anyone. For those with few resources, lotteries appear to offer the chance of relief from their circumstances. But the actual chance of winning anything substantial is slight. |
| | Some people in society have addictions to gambling, and lotteries feed that addiction. Gambling addiction is a significant social problem. The government has no business capitalizing on such problems. |
| | Ads for lotteries appeal to the dream of easy money. These ads are misleading, because they make it seem as if winning the lottery is easy. They encourage people to spend their hard-earned money on a one-in-a-million chance at wealth. |
| | Lotteries also place young people at risk. A US study indicated that state-run lotteries tended to increase participation by juveniles in all forms of gambling, legal or illegal. Is this the future we want for our young people? |

C. **In your notebook, indicate how you would arrange the paragraphs arguing for government-run lotteries in Part B if you were writing for**
- **a sympathetic audience**
- **a hostile audience**

**Do the same for the arguments against government-run lotteries.**

When writing business memos, reports, or other work-related documents, keep in mind the needs of your audience and your purpose in writing.

- Most business readers are very busy and must process large amounts of information. Therefore, state important information and any actions you expect your readers to take at the beginning of the document. Fill in details later on. For example, memos should begin with a clear, specific subject line, while reports should often have an executive summary that includes the major findings or recommendations.

- Structure your document to make it easy to find information. Use appropriate headings, bullets, and numbered lists to help your reader navigate through the document.

- Use graphics, such as charts, graphs, and diagrams, to summarize or clarify detailed information. Number each graphic, and refer to the number at the appropriate spot in the text.

**A. Write a subject line for the following memo that is clear and specific. Suggest an appropriate heading for each of the last three paragraphs.**

## Tasty Food Company

To:        All Employees
From:    Karl Stewart, Office Manager

Subject:   _____

October 16, 2004

Please be advised that, effective immediately, the company will be instituting strict procedures aimed at limiting employee workplace viral infection transmission. This winter has seen an extraordinary number of such infections in the community. Proper hygiene on the part of every employee is essential if we are to contain the spread of illness in our offices. Management therefore requests that employees wash their hands frequently, stay home when necessary, and observe proper procedures in the preparation of food products.

Management requires that all employees wash their hands before eating, visiting the cafeteria, or after going to the washroom. Proper handwashing technique involves the removal of all jewellery from the fingers, the application of lukewarm water to the hands, followed by a liberal application of disinfectant soap. Particular attention should be paid to the fingertips and the areas between the fingers. Dry hands with a paper towel; then, use the paper towels as protection when turning off the taps, to avoid reinfection.

In addition to the contractually allowed ten days of sick leave per calendar year, management encourages employees who show signs of illness to work at home. No sick leave days will be deducted as long as employees inform their manager of their intention. This measure should minimize the early-stage infection risk of an illness.

Management wishes to reinforce the need for extra caution on the part of those employees who are in direct contact with food products. Appropriate hygienic worker apparel—hair nets, latex gloves, and clean gowns—should be worn at all times by those in the food-production work areas. We are all proud of our record for safety and good hygiene; continual vigilance will ensure that this reputation is upheld.

**B. In your notebook, identify one place in the preceding memo where a graphic might be helpful, and describe what the graphic would be (or provide a sketch).**

**C. Identify one place in the memo where a bulleted list could be used to organize information more clearly. Rewrite the list in your notebook.**

**Plain language** is a technique of writing and presenting information that is appropriate and accessible to the intended reader. Its use is becoming more and more popular in business and government documents. The following principles of plain language are applicable to all forms of business writing.

- Avoid jargon (see Lesson 8) and use technical terms only if you are sure all of your readers will understand them.

    EXAMPLE:   **Technical:** With a price increase of $2 per unit, <u>market elasticity</u> will decrease, which will reduce <u>plant efficiency</u> and increase the <u>marginal cost per unit</u>.
    **Revised:** With a price increase of $2 per unit, sales will fall. Since the costs of running the plant will stay the same, we will actually be spending more to produce each unit.

- Keep sentences and paragraphs short, cut out unnecessary words, and avoid using long strings of nouns.

    EXAMPLES:   **Wordy:** The <u>decision</u> of the committee was to proceed with <u>the implementation of</u> the plan.
    **Revised:** The committee decided to proceed with the plan.
    **Noun String:** We offer an <u>employee bonus incentive</u> plan.
    **Revised:** We offer a <u>bonus plan</u> as an <u>incentive</u> for <u>employees</u>.

- Maintain a formal yet conversational tone. Write memos or directives in the second person (you); for most technical and scientific reports, use the third person (he, she, it, one). Avoid colloquial or slang expressions, and maintain a high standard for spelling and grammar. Finally, read your work out loud. If you do not feel comfortable speaking the words you have written, then simplify them.

**D. Choose one paragraph from the memo in Part A, and rewrite it on the lines that follow using the plain language guidelines given above.**

_____

_____

_____

_____

_____

_____

_____

_____

_____

_____

_____

_____

## Integrating Quotations

> ■ One way to use quotations in an essay or report is to integrate the quoted words into your own sentence. When you choose this method, make sure that the sentence containing the quotation makes grammatical sense. If it doesn't, try changing the sentence to fit the quotation.
>
> EXAMPLES: **Poorly Integrated:** Many Aboriginal peoples believed that "It was a common belief that the northern lights were the reflections in the sky of huge fires in the distant north, or that the mighty God himself lighted up the dark and cold parts of the world."
>
> **Correct:** Among Aboriginal peoples, "It was a common belief that the northern lights were the reflections in the sky of huge fires in the distant north, or that the mighty God himself lighted up the dark and cold parts of the world."
>
> **Correct:** A common belief of Aboriginal peoples was "that the northern lights were the reflections in the sky of huge fires in the distant north, or that the mighty God himself lighted up the dark and cold parts of the world." [Source: "Auroral Mythology," http://www.northern-lights.no/english/mythology/index.shtml]

**A.** **Change each of the following sentences to integrate the quotation correctly. Do not change the quotations. Use proofreader's marks.**

**1.** Candace Savage, in her article "Night Spirits," compares the aurora borealis (northern lights) to: "Like whitecaps on a storm-tossed sea, the northern lights are the visible crests of invisible plasma waves that batter Earth."

**2.** Franck Pettersen suggests that "And they really remind us of draperies or curtains which are flickering in the wind." [Source: "Aurora Borealis" by Franck Pettersen]

**3.** In "The Ballad of the Northern Lights," Robert Service conjures up images of a celestial war, with "Pennants of silver waved and streamed, lazy banners unfurled; / Sudden splendors of sabres gleamed, lightning javelins were hurled."

**4.** Legends of the Saulteau, Kwakiutl, and Tlingit Nations all explained the northern lights "the dancing of human spirits." [Source: http://vathena.arc.nasa.gov/curric/space/aurora/aurfolk.html]

**B.** **Write a sentence in your notebook in which you integrate part of the following quotation.**

"According to some people, the aurora swishes, hisses, sizzles, rustles, rushes, whizzes, crackles, or whispers. It can sound like the tearing of silk, the wind in the trees, the noise of flying birds, the sweeping of sand, or the flapping of a ship's sails. Or it can sound like nothing at all and, in fact, many northerners have insisted that the aurora is soundless, and have questioned the claims of successful auroral auditors."

[Source: "The Noisy Aurora?" by W.R. Hunt, *The Alaska Science Forum*]

> - Another method of integrating quotations is to provide an introductory sentence, followed by a colon. The introductory sentence usually provides background for, and summarizes the main idea of, the quotation.
>
>   EXAMPLE:   As Franck Pettersen points out, our fascination with the aurora borealis crosses the boundary between art and science: "The northern lights are poetry, they are nature's light show, and they are quantum leaps in the oxygen atom. They are elementary particle physics, superstition, mythology, and fairy tales."   [Source: "Aurora Borealis" by Franck Pettersen]

**C.** **In your notebook, write an introductory sentence for the following excerpt from Ken Dryden's tribute to legendary Montréal Canadiens captain Maurice Richard. In your introduction, include a brief summary of the main idea of the quotation.**

He was the archetypal goal scorer. He didn't do it surgically, with long-range bombs like Bobby Hull, with Wayne Gretzky's deception, with Mike Bossy's precision, or with Mario Lemieux's dazzling moves. Goal scoring for Richard was basic and elemental, less an act of skill and more an act of will.
[Source: "Farewell to the Rocket," *Time*, June 12, 2000.]

> - When you use a direct quotation, make sure that you are not changing the original meaning of the passage by taking it out of context.
>
>   EXAMPLE:   **Out of Context:** Ken Dryden dismisses Richard's goal-scoring ability as "basic and elemental," not like the "dazzling moves" of great players like Mario Lemieux.
>
>   **In Context:** Ken Dryden suggests Richard's "basic and elemental" goal-scoring ability compares favourably with the "dazzling moves" of Mario Lemieux.

**D.** **The sentences below include quoted words from the following excerpt. Write <u>C</u> if the quotation accurately reflects the meaning of the original. Write <u>X</u> if the quotation has been taken out of its original context.**

NHL salaries for the boys who play the game have grown so astronomical that only the Hubble telescope knows for sure what some of them are getting. The hustle in professional hockey has long since ceased to be the hustle of those who love the game for its own sake and for the sake of the country or the city they may be said to represent. Professional hockey waves the flag for the same reason that the beer companies who sponsor hockey drench themselves in maple leaf emblems. Marketing. [Source: "Ice Hockey" by Rex Murphy on *The National*, January 10, 2003. From the CBC Web site, http://www.cbc.ca/national/rex/rex20030110.html]

1. Rex Murphy claims that "the hustle in professional hockey has long since ceased...." _____

2. Murphy praises professional hockey teams that "[wave] the flag" and "drench themselves in maple leaf emblems." _____

3. He admires the professional hockey players, who he claims "love the game for its own sake and for the sake of the country or the city they may be said to represent." _____

4. Mr. Murphy worries that NHL players' salaries "have grown so astronomical that only the Hubble telescope knows for sure what some of them are getting." _____

## Proofreading

> - The last stage of the writing process is proofreading. **Proofreading** involves checking spelling, grammar, punctuation, and capitalization.
> - Although most word-processing software features tools that can help you with your writing—such as a spell-check feature, a dictionary, and a thesaurus—most errors are easier to find on paper than on screen. Also, remember that spell-check programs will not find all errors. Grammar-check programs are not perfect either. Therefore, when you reach the proofreading stage of the writing process, you may find it helpful to print out a hard copy of your work and use proofreader's marks to show changes needed in your writing.

**A.** **Write a corrected version of the following passage using the proofreader's marks as a guide.**

Do you know who you are? Can you prove it/ that may seem like an odd question,
But for some unlucky Canadians, it's too all real. They are victims of identity theft, the
newest and fastest-growing form of fraud in the digital digital age.
¶ "There's been an explosion in identity theft in the passed few years," says RCMP Inspector
John Sliter. Approximately 20,000 new cases of identity theft are reported to the rCMP
every year by credit burreaus. And about 1.4 million false Social Insurance cards in are
circulation, according to the Social Insurance Registry. Some estimates claim as many as
one in five familys in the United States may have been targets of identity frauds.

**B. Use proofreader's marks to correct the passage that follows.**

How can someone steal your idenity? Its really not that hard. In fact, there are many ways todo it. One commonly used scam

is to place a news paper ad promiseing applicants overseas employment If you respond to one these of ads, you will be asked to, send along a copy of your birth certificate, diploma, driver's licence, or other documents. That's all the theif needs to startbuilding a new new identity. **[12 errors]**

Some potential fraud artists simply submit a chnage-of-adress form at the post office. suddenly, all your mail will be redirected to wherrever the thief requests. others simply look through your garbage for credit-card applications bank cheques, or other personal information. Then, it's just matter of using your personal information to applying for credit. **[9 errors]**

In the future. high-tech iris scans and and voice printing may make it harder for thiefes to pretend they are Someone else. Right now, though there's not a lot you can do to pervent this kind of theft. As one authority put it, "Forgeries are very, very good these days. **[7 errors]**

Experts recommend giving out never personal information over the phone especially your birth date or SOcial Insurance Number—and checking the credenshals of any company that make's such a request. they also advise shredding any bills or papers that might personal information before throwing them out. **[7 errors]**

**C. Choose one paragraph from Part B and rewrite it below, incorporating the corrections you marked.**

_____

_____

_____

_____

_____

_____

_____

**Read the excerpt below from "My Canada" by Tomson Highway, and then answer the questions that follow.**

Where else in the world can you travel by bus, automobile, or train (and the odd ferry) for ten, twelve, or fourteen days straight and see a landscape that changes so dramatically, so spectacularly. The Newfoundland coast with its white foam and roar; the red sand beaches of Prince Edward Island; the graceful curves and slopes of Cape Breton's Cabot Trail; the rolling dairy land of south shore Québec; the peerless, uncountable maple-bordered lakes of Ontario; the haunting north shore of Lake Superior; the wheat fields of Manitoba and Saskatchewan; the ranch land of Alberta; the mountain ranges, valleys, and lush rainforests of the West Coast. The list could go on for ten pages, and still only cover the southern section of the country, a sliver of land compared with the North, whose immensity is almost unimaginable....

Of course Canada has its problems. We'd like to lower our crime rate, but it is under relative control, and, the fact is, we live in a safe country. We struggle with our health-care system, trying to find a balance between universality and affordability. But no person in this country is denied medical care for lack of money, no child need go without a vaccination. Oh yes, we have our concerns, but in the global scheme of things we are so well off. Have you ever stopped to look at the oranges and apples piled high as mountains in supermarkets from Sicamous, British Columbia, to Twillingate, Newfoundland? Have you paused to think about the choice of meat, fish, vegetables, cheese, bread, cereals, cookies, chips, dips, and pop we have? Or even about the number of banks, clothing stores, and restaurants?

And think of our history. For the greater part, the pain and violence, tragedy, horror, and evil that have scarred forever the history of too many countries are largely absent from our past. There's no denying we've had our trials and times of shame, but dark though they may have been, they pale by comparison with events that have shaped many other nations.

Our cities, too, are gems. Take Toronto, where I have chosen to live. My adopted city never fails to thrill me with its racial, linguistic, cultural—not to mention lifestyle—diversity. On any ordinary day on the city's streets and subway, in stores and restaurants, I can hear the muted ebb and flow—the sweet chorus—of twenty different tongues. At any time of day, I can feast on food from six different continents, from Greek souvlaki to Thai mango salad, from Italian prosciutto to French bouillabaisse, from Ecuadorian empanada to Jamaican jerk chicken, from Indian lamb curry to Chinese lobster in ginger and green onion (with a side order of greens in oyster sauce). Indeed, one could probably eat in restaurants every week for a year and never have to eat of the same cuisine twice.

And do all these people get along? Well, they all live in a situation of relative harmony, co-operation, and peace. They certainly aren't terrorizing, torturing, and massacring one another.... Dislike—rancour—may exist in pockets here and there, but not, I believe, hatred on the scale of such blistering intensity that we see elsewhere. Is Canada a successful experiment in racial harmony and peaceful co-existence? Yes, I would say so, proudly.

Much as I often love and admire the countries I visit and their people, I can't help but notice when I go abroad that most people in France look French, most in Italy, Italian. In Sweden they look Swedish and in Japan they look Japanese. Beautiful, absolutely beautiful. But where's the variety? I ask myself. Where's the mix, the spice, the funk?

Well, it's here, right here in Canada—my Canada. When I, as an aboriginal citizen of this country, find myself thinking about all the people we've received into this homeland of mine, this beautiful country, when I think of the millions of people we've given safe haven to, following agony, terror, hunger, and great sadness in their own home countries, well, my little Cree heart just puffs up with pride. And I walk the streets of Toronto, the streets of Canada, the streets of my home, feeling tall as a maple.  [Source: Excerpted from "My Canada" by Tomson Highway. *Imperial Oil Review*, July 28, 2001. http: www.imperialoil.ca/thisis/publications/review/mycanada.htm]

A.  Is the purpose of the passage argumentative or persuasive? Explain.

_____

_____

B.  Do you think the author is writing primarily for a hostile or a receptive audience? Explain.

_____

_____

C.  Identify three examples of emotional appeals in the passage.

_____

_____

_____

D.  Underline the topic sentence in paragraphs 2, 3, 4, and 5. (Note: Not all the topic sentences are in the usual location).

E.  Identify what main type of evidence—reasons, facts, or examples—is used to support each topic sentence you chose in Part D.

Paragraph 2: _____

Paragraph 3: _____

Paragraph 4: _____

Paragraph 5: _____

F.  Identify the pattern of development of the whole passage. _____

G.  Identify three specific examples that show how the author creates coherence.

_____

_____

_____

H.  Write a thesis that sums up the main idea of the passage.

_____

_____

I.  Provide three examples that indicate the passage is written informally.

_____

_____

_____

**A.** **Write your own short essay titled "My Canada." Your purpose and audience are similar to those of Tomson Highway in his piece of the same title (see page 108). The tone should be formal. Include the following in your essay:**

1. An introduction that grabs the reader and includes a thesis sentence.

2. At least three paragraphs, each containing a topic sentence that supports the thesis.

3. Supporting details in the form of facts, arguments, and examples.

4. A quotation from the Tomson Highway passage on page 108 that is integrated into the text.

5. A conclusion that summarizes your main arguments.

**B. In your notebook, rewrite the following memo to make it more accessible and appropriate for a business audience. Follow the steps below.**

1. Identify the most important information in the memo, and then write an opening paragraph that contains this information. Cross out sentences in other paragraphs that repeat this information.

2. Identify information in the memo that would be clearer in list form. Rewrite the information as a list.

3. Use proofreader's marks to simplify wording, shorten long sentences, reword long strings of nouns, replace jargon, and switch sentences to first or second person.

4. Replace the subject line with a more informative and specific description of the contents.

5. Suggest headings that could improve the clarity of the memo.

# dot.COMcepts, Inc.

**MEMO**

TO:         All staff
FROM:       J. Harlow, Human Resources Development Manager
SUBJECT:    A Date to Remember

February 10, 2003

Improvisation is a type of theatre in which actors perform without a script. A variety of so-called "theatre games" are used as the basis for a scene, which is further developed using suggestions from the audience. The actors must then create a scene on the spot. Doing improv is exhilarating and fun; at the same time, it challenges the performers to work co-operatively and promotes the values of acceptance, teamwork, and risk-taking.

These same qualities are essential aspects of a healthy and successful business-oriented enterprise. Therefore, as part of our ongoing employee development program, this year's team-building exercise will take place on Friday, February 23. Pretty As a Picture, a group of experienced performers who specialize in business performance workshop presentations, will lead employees through an exciting improvisation workshop.

All employees are invited and encouraged to attend. The agenda for the day is as follows: We will meet in Boardroom A at 8:45 a.m. Coffee and pastries will be available. From 9:00 until 10:00, Pretty As a Picture will present a demonstration of improv comedy, using suggestions from employees. At 10:00, we will break up into small groups for theatre games. Lunch will be from 12:00 to 1:00 p.m. Sandwiches will be supplied in Boardroom B. From 1:00 to 3:00 we will return to our groups for more improv exercises. Then, at 3:00, all the groups will come together again for a joint performance. From 4:00 to 5:00, we will evaluate the workshop. President Mark Ali will lead a discussion of how we can apply the lessons we have learned to improve the performance and operation of the company.

In order to facilitate the ordering of food and supplies, it is requested that all interested parties contact the events co-ordinator directly at extension 350 before February 20 to confirm your intention to attend. It is to be hoped that everyone can be present for what should be a constructive and informative day.

- **Primary research** is information gathered from first-hand sources. When researching an historical event, original documents written at the time the event took place—such as newspaper reports or government bills—are primary resources. For a paper on an historical figure, you might look at his or her letters, diaries, memoirs, or other writings.
- Primary research also includes experiments you perform and experiences you undergo. For example, your primary research on Canada's health system might include a visit to an Emergency ward. If you are writing about a particular book, reading the book itself is primary research. In social studies, you might conduct a survey or experiment as part of your primary research.
- **Secondary research** is information gathered second-hand. Encyclopedias, books on your topic written by other researchers, biographies, critical interpretations, and reviews can all be secondary sources of information.
- You do not always need to consult primary resources when writing a paper, unless you are writing about a literary work.

**A. Identify each resource below as P for primary or S for secondary.**

Topic: The Great Depression

1. Interviewing someone who lived through the Depression _____
2. *The Great Depression* by Pierre Berton _____
3. Statistics on unemployment from the 1936 Census of Canada _____
4. The lyrics of songs sung by unemployed men during the Depression _____
5. A recent journal article about the causes of the Great Depression _____

**B. Use your library catalogue, the Internet, and your own knowledge to list one primary and one secondary resource for each of the following topics.**

| Topic | Primary Resource | Secondary Resource |
|---|---|---|
| **1.** The disappearance of the ship *The Edmund Fitzgerald* on Lake Superior | | |
| **2.** The theme of "survival" in Canadian literature | | |
| **3.** The Group of Seven | | |
| **4.** The September 11, 2001, terrorist attacks on the United States | | |
| **5.** The life of Pierre Elliott Trudeau | | |

- Non-fiction books are arranged on library shelves according to call numbers.
- In the **Dewey decimal system**, which is used in many public and secondary school libraries, each book is assigned a number from 000 to 999, according to its subject matter.

| | |
|---|---|
| 000–099 Reference | 500–599 Science and Math |
| 100–199 Philosophy | 600–699 Technology |
| 200–299 Religion | 700–799 The Arts |
| 300–399 Social Science | 800–899 Literature |
| 400–499 Languages | 900–999 History and Geography |

- Many college and university libraries use the **Library of Congress (LC) Classification System**. This system uses a series of letters followed by numbers to classify a book. The numbers following the letters further specify the subject matter and location of the book. The main lettered categories used in the system are described below.

| | | | | |
|---|---|---|---|---|
| A | General Works | N | Fine Arts |
| B | Philosophy, Psychology, Religion | P | Language and Literature |
| C–F | History | Q | Science |
| G | Geography, Anthropology, Recreation | R | Medicine |
| H | Social Science | S | Agriculture |
| J | Political Science | T | Technology |
| K | Law | U | Military Science |
| L | Education | V | Naval Science |
| M | Music | Z | Bibliography, Library Science, Information Resources |

**A.** **Identify the Dewey decimal (DD) number range and the Library of Congress (LC) letter range for each of the following topics.**

| Subject | DD | LC |
|---|---|---|
| **1.** Physical geography of the Plains region | | |
| **2.** Buddhism | | |
| **3.** Scientific discoveries in the twentieth century | | |
| **4.** Canadian literature | | |
| **5.** The works of Michelangelo | | |

**B.** **Use the online catalogue of a college or university you are interested in attending to answer the following questions in your notebook. If the college or university has more than one library, choose one branch only.**

1. Which system does this library use: the Dewey decimal or Library of Congress Classification system?
2. In addition to book lending, list three other services offered to members of this library.
3. Where are the periodicals kept at this library?
4. Find the title and call number of a book on job hunting.
5. Find the title and call number of a book on the composer Ludwig van Beethoven.

# Lesson
## 68 — Internet Search Techniques

- Most search engines on the Internet allow you to use the **Boolean search** terms—AND, OR, and NOT—to narrow or broaden your search.
  - Use **AND** to find pages that contain more than one key word. Some search engines treat any string of key words as an AND query. In others, you must specify this type of search. Some search engines provide a "match all" option. If you use this option, you do not need to use AND.

    EXAMPLE: **saturn AND car** will find all the pages that include both these terms
  - Use **OR** to find pages that contain either of two or more key words.

    EXAMPLE: **football OR soccer** will produce all the pages about football (which is what soccer is called in many countries) and all the pages about soccer. In some search engines, OR searches are available as a "match any" option.
  - Use **NOT** to narrow a search by excluding sites containing another term.

    EXAMPLE: **saturn NOT car** will eliminate all pages related to the Saturn automobile, making it easier to find those that deal with the planet Saturn

- Some search engines allow you to perform an **exact phrase search** by enclosing the phrase in quotation marks.

  EXAMPLE: **"to be or not to be"** will find only pages where all six words appear together in this order. Without the quotation marks, some engines assume you are doing an AND search.

- In some systems, placing an **asterisk** after a word or part of a word allows you to search for all word forms that contain the letters you typed.

  EXAMPLE: The key word **quebe\*** will find all sites containing Québec, Québecker, and Québécois.

---

**A. Circle the search string in each group that will likely yield the most useful results.**

1. Search: Information on the original 1968 version of the movie *Planet of the Apes* (directed by Franklin J. Schaffner and starring Charlton Heston), not the 2001 remake directed by Tim Burton and starring Mark Wahlberg.
   - (a) "planet of the apes" AND schaffner NOT burton
   - (b) planet of the apes AND "heston NOT wahlberg"
   - (c) "planet of the apes AND schaffner AND heston"

2. Search: Information on someone called Steven (or Stephen) Martin. Eliminate sites about the famous comedian Steve Martin.
   - (a) "ste\* martin"
   - (b) "steven martin" OR "stephen martin" NOT steve
   - (c) "ste\* martin" NOT comedian

**B. Choose the correct search query from the box to answer each question below.**

| | |
|---|---|
| (a) "zebra mussels great lakes" | (c) "zebra mussels" OR "great lakes" |
| (b) "zebra mussels" AND "great lakes" | (d) zebra OR mussels OR great OR lakes |

1. Which search query above would yield the most hits? _____
2. Which would yield the fewest hits? _____
3. Which search query is most likely to produce useful information about the problem of zebra mussels invading the Great Lakes? _____

---

 **Unit 6, Research and Study Skills**

## Evaluating Internet Sources

- There is an extensive amount of information available on the Internet, but not all of it is reliable. For this reason, it is important to evaluate Internet sources critically.
- The first step in evaluating an Internet source is to find out who created it and the reason it was created (its purpose). Each of the five types of Web sites listed below can provide useful information.

| Type of Web Site | Publisher (Sponsor) | Purpose | URL Address |
|---|---|---|---|
| Personal | individuals | to entertain or inform | may include a tilde (~) |
| Advocacy | organizations | to persuade the public to adopt a point of view or support a cause | often ends in **.org** |
| Business/Marketing | companies | to sell products or services | often ends **.com** |
| News | broadcasters or newspapers | to inform; usually provides up-to-the-minute information | often ends **.com** |
| Informational | universities or governments | to inform | often ends **.edu** or **.gov** |

**A.** **Find one Canadian example to illustrate each of the five types of Web sites above. Record the URL, the name of the sponsoring individual or organization, and the purpose of the site.**

Personal: _____

_____

Advocacy: _____

_____

Business: _____

_____

News: _____

_____

Informational: _____

_____

The second step in evaluating Internet sources is to consider the authority, accuracy, timeliness, and scope of the site.

- **Authority** Is the author or sponsor clearly identified? Does the author or sponsor have any credentials that qualify him or her to speak on the topic? Is the information provided based on research, or compiled from other secondary sources?
- **Accuracy** Does the page list sources of factual information? Is it free from typographical, grammatical, or spelling errors? Can the information presented be verified through other sources? Does the information or argument presented make sense?
- **Timeliness** Does the page contain information about when it was last updated? Has it been updated recently?
- **Scope** Does the page provide enough detailed information to be useful? Are there gaps in the information presented?

**B. Find three Web sites that provide information for a report on the problems caused by zebra mussels in the Great Lakes. Evaluate each Web site for its authority, accuracy, timeliness, and scope. Give specific examples to back up your evaluation.**

- The third step in evaluating Web sites is to look for signs of bias. **Bias** is the distortion of information by emphasizing certain facts or perspectives and ignoring or omitting others. For example, a Web site whose purpose is to persuade you to do or believe something may present biased information.
- Note that biased information is not necessarily incorrect; it is more likely to be incomplete. For example, the manufacturer of Williams' Widgets is not likely to tell you about the new improved widget that Wanda's Widgets has just introduced; for that information, you will have to go to another site. That is why it is important to check several different sources to get a variety of viewpoints on a topic.
- Personal Web sites cover a wide range of topics, but the information they provide is not always balanced. It is important to verify the information on these sites by checking other, more reliable print or Internet sources.
- Business and advocacy sites often provide good information, but it is not necessarily unbiased. Check other sources for alternative viewpoints.
- Informational and news Web sites generally provide the most balanced information. However, it is still good to check other sources.

**C. Choose one of the Web sites you listed in Part A, and identify any examples of bias (e.g., missing or incomplete information; unsupported statements in favour of, or against, something or someone). Write a brief bias evaluation in your notebook.**

[Source: Lesson material adapted from Jan Alexander and Marsha Ann Tate, Wolfgram Memorial Library, Widener University, and http://www.infopeople.org, "Evaluating Internet Resources: A Checklist."]

## Posing Research Questions (KWL Charts)

- One method of organizing a research project is with a KWL chart. KWL stands for What I **K**now, What I **W**ant to Know, and What I **L**earned. Complete the first column with everything you already know about your subject. Any gaps in your knowledge or questions that arise as you complete the first column should be recorded in the second column. The questions in the second column become the focus questions for your research, which is then summarized in the third column.

- As you do research to fill in the third column, you may come up with further questions, which can be added to the second column. When you have accumulated enough information to answer your questions, use the information you have gathered to write an outline and a first draft.

- KWL charts can also be used as a study aid. When preparing for a test or exam, begin by filling in the first column with what you remember about the subject. In the second column, write questions you want to answer. Then, read your notes to find the missing information. Reading with a purpose will help you to focus on the important information.

| What I KNOW | What I WANT to Know | What I LEARNED |
| --- | --- | --- |
| | | |

**Choose a topic from one of your classes this term. Then, fill in the KWL chart below by completing the activities that follow.**

| What I KNOW | What I WANT to Know | What I LEARNED |
| --- | --- | --- |
| | | |

1. In point form, fill in the first column with all the information you remember about the topic.

2. In question form, list in the second column facts you are unsure of, and aspects of the topic that you need to review. You should have at least three questions.

3. Review your notes and any other sources necessary to find answers to your questions. Record the information in point form in the third column.

4. Evaluate the KWL chart as a study aid. Did you find it helpful? In what way?

_____

_____

**Clustering** (or webbing) and **outlining** are useful tools both for taking notes and for organizing ideas before you write.

■ Creating a cluster diagram or web is a way to visually represent how ideas are related. Write your main topic in a circle in the middle of your page. Write subtopics in their own circles, connected to the main topic with lines. Information or supporting details can be added to the cluster with smaller circles.

EXAMPLE: The following cluster diagram outlines the main ideas in the paragraph in Lesson 62, Part A, on page 100.

**A.** Create a cluster diagram in your notebook to organize ideas for an essay describing your study habits. Include at least four circles attached to the main topic circle.

**B.** Create a cluster diagram in the space below to show the advantages of using virtual-reality systems to treat panic disorders. Use information from the following excerpt.

Part of what makes virtual reality successful [as a treatment for panic disorders]…is the increased realism. With traditional phobia therapy, patients are encouraged to imagine the situation that they fear and then practise relaxing.

The problem is many people's imaginations aren't strong enough to truly conjure the situation….

Virtual reality, in contrast, gives patients a much more intense stimulus….

Virtual reality also lets the therapist have much more control over the experience. When treating fear of flying, the therapist can use the simulator to ease someone into the experience—having the plane taxi for a long time and take off only when the patient feels ready.

That's impossible to do in real life, "unless you rent a 747 for the afternoon so you can practise flying—which is a little expensive for the average patient," jokes Charles Pierce, a Kitchener psychologist who recently bought a virtual-reality system.

Pierce's simulator costs $150 an hour and patients can take off and land as many times as they want. As well, Pierce remains alongside the patient—another thing that's impossible in real life, unless he or she can afford to pay for a therapist to accompany him or her on a flight.   [Source: "Virtual Therapy, Real Results" by Clive Thompson]

- **Outlining** is another graphic approach to organizing ideas. As you read or gather information, try to arrange topics, subtopics, and supporting details as shown in the example below. Use roman numerals (e.g., I., II.) for main topics, capital letters (e.g., A., B.) for subtopics, and arabic numerals (e.g., 1., 2.) for supporting details.

  EXAMPLE:  I. The beaver is an appropriate symbol for Canada
         A. Historical role
            1. Was country's most precious commodity in 18$^{th}$ c.
            2. Almost became extinct due to fur trade
         B. Desirable traits
            1. Ingenuity
            2. Hard work
            3. Adaptability

**C.** **Make an outline based on the cluster diagram you created in Part A.**

**D.** **The following notes contain three main ideas, along with subtopics and supporting details. Rearrange the notes into a cluster diagram or outline. (If you need more space, write your answer in your notebook.) Hint: Start by identifying the three main ideas.**

Topic: The Canadian workplace has undergone some fundamental changes over the last few decades.

- Some workers prefer part-time, contract, or self-employment arrangements, but many are in these situations involuntarily.
- Untrained health-care aides are replacing more highly paid registered nurses.
- Middle-management and supervisory positions have been cut to make companies more competitive.
- Non-standard work arrangements have become more common.
- Therefore, employers tend to hire consultants rather than keeping specialists on staff.
- Other employees have taken on responsibilities of fired managers without any increase in pay or status.
- Middle-class, middle-income jobs are disappearing.
- Employers tend to prefer generalists over specialists.
- Employers want people with broad skills that can be applied to different jobs.
- Approximately one-third of Canadians do not have full-time, long-term employment.
- Communications, interpersonal, and analytical skills are useful in a wide range of jobs.
- Specialists are less flexible and tend to be more expensive.

- **Paraphrasing** means restating what the original author said using different words. A paraphrase is usually about the same length as the original.

- Use phrases such as "The author states...," "She goes on to describe...," and "He seems to feel that..." to make it clear that you are stating someone else's ideas.

- Avoid using the same phrasing as the original, unless there is no other acceptable way to express the idea. If you do borrow the same phrasing, use quotation marks.

EXAMPLE: **Original**: The one constant thing about all art is that it is forever changing. There have been countless changes in the long history of art. The most significant have been brought about by the genius of a single artist. Some changes have come about through the invention of new media and new techniques—say, the birth of mosaic, manuscript illumination, oil paint, or perspective. Other changes have come about because a young artist threw aside all traditions and depicted his or her world in a fresh, different, and completely new way. Leonardo Da Vinci was one such revolutionary. So was Claude Monet. And Pablo Picasso, of course. [Source: *Art for Dummies* by Thomas Hoving]

**Paraphrase:** Hoving suggests that change is the only thing about art that is constant. The history of art, he claims, is full of examples of changes, the most important of which are introduced by individual artistic geniuses. Hoving cites some changes inspired by new inventions or techniques (mosaic, illuminated manuscripts, oil paint, and perspective, for example), and attributes others to the revolutionary vision of artists like Da Vinci, Monet, and Picasso, who reject the old way of doing things and discover a new vision of the world.

## A. Paraphrase the following two excerpts.

1. The secret to becoming a *connoisseur*, someone who recognizes artistic quality in all its subtle variations, is simple. You look and look more and look again. That's what the best of the pros do. The secret is being saturated in art. Almost anyone can become an art expert with the right amount of saturation. And only by saturation of the original art itself, not through books, or gazing at photographs, or attending slide lectures, or taking copious notes at seminars. You will gain expertise and authority (and confidence) simply by soaking up physically all the art your eyes can digest.

[Source: *Art for Dummies* by Thomas Hoving]

_____

_____

_____

_____

_____

**2.** Some people are very excited about the idea of the e-book, but I can't for the life of me see why. What could possibly be exciting about looking at a little laptop screen? The emotional connection we have with books is not generated by the words alone. The book itself—the physical object—also has a great deal to do with it. We feel pride in a library. Is it possible to feel such pride in a shelf of e-novels lined up in their little plastic cases? Books come in all shapes and sizes, with attractive, colourful covers that elicit an emotional response. We give books as gifts, lend them out, share them with friends. E-books remind me of Campbell's soup tins—they all look alike. Would you be tempted to buy someone the file of Margaret Atwood's latest novel, or introduce a child to *Alice in Wonderland* online?

[Source: "Gutenberg Can Rest in Peace" by Pierre Renaud]

---

- When you **summarize**, you provide a brief overview of the main point an author makes. As with paraphrasing, you should use your own words as much as possible. A summary is much shorter and more general than a paraphrase. The following is a summary of the original passage on the previous page.

  EXAMPLE:    Hoving suggests that changes are happening constantly in the world of art. Two main sources of change are new inventions or techniques (such as mosaic or perspective), and the inspiration of individual artists who reject the status quo and offer us a new way of seeing the world.

**B. Summarize both excerpts in Part A.**

**1.** _____

**2.** _____

> - When you use another person's ideas in an essay, you must give them credit. Failure to do so is called **plagiarism**. You need to acknowledge your source not only for direct quotations, but also for ideas or information that you have paraphrased or summarized.
> - At the end of a research paper, report, or essay, you must include a **bibliography**. The format of the entries will vary slightly, depending on the style your teacher directs you to use. Two popular formats are the Modern Languages Association (MLA) style for literature and the humanities, and the American Psychological Association (APA) style for the sciences. Some examples of entries from both of these sources are shown in the Appendix at the back of this book. For more complete information, consult a style guide.

**In your notebook, create a bibliography using all of the sources below. Follow the order and format specified by your teacher.**

A book edited by Harold Bloom called *Emily Bronte's Wuthering Heights*. Published in 1987 by Chelsea House publishers of New York

An article on pages 119–136 of the book mentioned above, titled "Baby-Work: The Myth of Rebirth in *Wuthering Heights*," by Stevie Davies

*The Lighthearted Cookbook* by Anne Lindsay. Published by Key Porter Books of Toronto, in 1988

An article in *The Globe and Mail* titled "Northern Cod Officially Declared Endangered." It appeared on page A13 of the Saturday paper on May 3, 2003. The author was Alanna Mitchell.

*The Complete Guide to Home Wiring*. No author is given. Published by Creative Publishing International of Chanhassen, Minnesota, in 2001

"Reality Check on Missile Defense," an article by David Rudd, posted on May 4, 2003, in the *Winnipeg Free Press* online. The article was accessed on May 6, 2003 at http://www.winnipegfreepress.com/westview/index.html.

*A Fine Balance* by Rohinton Mistry. Published in 1993 by McClelland & Stewart Inc. of Toronto

*Marketing Online for Dummies* by Bud Smith and Frank Catalano. Published in 1998 by IDG Books International (Foster City, California)

A videocassette of the movie *Persuasion*, starring Amanda Root and Ciarán Hinds. Directed by Roger Michell. It was released in DVD format by Columbia Tristar Home Video on February 1, 2000.

An article by Mary Janigan in *Maclean's* magazine, titled "The Debate Over ID Cards." It appeared on page 38 of the April 21, 2003 edition.

- Your bibliography gives a comprehensive list of the references you used in writing your paper. You also need to identify these sources right in the body of your essay or report. One way to do this is to put just enough information in parentheses to point the reader to the complete reference in your bibliography. (For an alternate way of citing sources in your work, see Lesson 75). These parenthetical notes are called **in-text citations**.

- Place the citation at the end of the phrase, clause, or sentence that contains the borrowed material. If your instructor does not specify a particular style for your citations, use MLA style for literature and humanities, and APA style for scientific papers. The appendix at the back of this book will give you some basic information about these styles. For more information, consult a style guide.

- You only need to include enough information for your reader to identify the source in the bibliography. So, if you have already mentioned some details, such as the name of the author or the title of the work in the body of your paper, you do not need to repeat that information in the parentheses.

**Write an in-text citation for each of the following and add necessary end punctuation. If no parenthetical information is necessary, just insert a period. The full reference for each source is found in Lesson 73. Use the citation style suggested by your teacher.**

1. **From page 6 of *The Complete Guide to Home Wiring***
   The *Complete Guide to Home Wiring* suggests that "a household electrical system can be compared with a home's plumbing system. Electrical current flows in wires in much the same way that water flows inside pipes. Both electricity and water enter the home, are distributed throughout the house, do their 'work,' and exit"

2. **From David Rudd's online article**
   In a recent article, David Rudd suggests that "If Canada lends a sense of perspective on what [the proposed North American missile defence system] can and cannot achieve…then it will be doing itself, its ally, and the broader international community a great and lasting service"

3. **From page 13 of *Marketing Online for Dummies***
   The authors of *Marketing Online for Dummies* describe the Internet as "a big mess—a mix of good and bad ideas, shaken, stirred, half-heated, and served buffet-style"

4. **From page 10 of *A Fine Balance***
   The main character in Rohinton Mistry's novel *A Fine Balance* is Dina Dalal. The first time we meet her, we are told that "sixteen years spent fending for herself had not hardened the looks which, a long time ago, used to make her brother's friends vie to impress her"

5. **From page 121 of Stevie Davies' essay on *Wuthering Heights***
   One commentator suggests that "Wuthering Heights…is an original myth of loss, exile, rebirth, and return"

## Footnotes and Endnotes

- One alternative to the in-text citation is to use footnotes or endnotes to document your sources.
- **Footnotes** generally contain the same information as a bibliography entry, with slightly different punctuation and arrangement. In addition, while bibliography entries do not usually include specific page numbers, footnote references do. Later references to the same source can be shortened, usually to the author's last name and a page number.
- **Endnotes** go on a separate page, titled Notes, at the end of the paper. They have the same content and similar format as footnotes (indent the first line and begin each note with a superscript number). However, endnotes should be double-spaced, not single-spaced. The appendix at the back of this book provides some basic information about the MLA style for footnotes and endnotes.
- When using footnotes or endnotes, you do not need to include an in-text citation. Instead, place a superscript number at the end of the quoted material, or at the end of the sentence or passage that contains information that needs to be acknowledged. Number each reference consecutively. The footnote or endnote begins with the same superscript number.

EXAMPLE:

"This same power that images had for Mary [Pratt] as a child drove her to paint when she was an adult. The way objects looked in different kinds of light struck her almost like a flash of lightning running through her body—the sunshine on a red bedspread, a codfish lying on tin foil, or the gleam of red currant jelly."[1]

[1] Jane Lind, *Mary and Christopher Pratt* (Vancouver: Douglas & MacIntyre, 1989) 21.

**Write consecutive footnote entries (numbered 1 to 5) for the five quotations in Lesson 74. Refer to the bibliographic entries in Lesson 73 for the information you need to complete the footnotes.**

**A.** Write <u>P</u> for primary source or <u>S</u> for secondary source next to each of the following resources, which are to be used for a report on animation in Canada.

1. Viewing films by famous Canadian animators _____

2. Reading a book about animation in Canada _____

3. Interviewing British Columbia animator Richard Condie, who created the Oscar-nominated film

   *The Big Snit* _____

4. Researching course offerings at various colleges that offer animation courses _____

5. Reading an interview with animator Carolyn Leaf in *Maclean's* magazine _____

**B.** Write the Dewey decimal system call-number range in which you would find each book. Then, write the initial Library of Congress Classification letter.

1. *Canadian Artists* _____

2. *The History of Language* _____

3. *Technological Solutions* _____

4. *Chemistry* _____

5. *The Sociology of Work* _____

**C.** Describe the results you would get using each of the following search queries.

1. improv* _____

   _____

2. Macintosh NOT computer _____

   _____

3. Macintosh AND computer _____

   _____

4. "lester b. pearson college of the pacific" _____

   _____

5. NAFTA OR "North American Free Trade Agreement" _____

   _____

**D. Write a paraphrase of the following passage.**

Part of the reason commercials are effective is that they are, in a sense, invisible. When you check the TV listings in your local newspaper or TV Guide, do you find the commercials listed? Since there will be 8 minutes of commercials in a 30-minute news show, would it not be relevant to indicate what the content of 27 percent of the show will be? But, of course, the commercials will not be listed. They are simply taken for granted, which is why so few people regard it as strange that a commercial should precede a news story about an earthquake in Chile, or, even worse, follow a news story about an earthquake in Chile. It is difficult to measure the effect on an audience that has been shown pictures of an earthquake's devastation, and immediately afterward is subjected to commercials for Gleem toothpaste, Scope, United Airlines, and Alka-Seltzer. Our best guess is that the earthquake takes on a surrealistic aspect; it is certainly trivialized. It is as if the program's producer is saying, "You needn't grieve or worry about what you are seeing. In a minute or so, we will make you happy with some good news about how to make your teeth whiter."     [Source: Neil Postman and Steve Powers, *How to Watch TV News* (New York: Penguin, 1992)  page 126.]

**E.  Now, write a summary of the excerpt in Part D.**

**F.  Create the following notations to acknowledge the source of the excerpt in Part D. Use MLA style, or the documentation style specified by your instructor.**

1. In-text citation: _____

2. Bibliography entry: _____

3. Footnote reference: _____

**A.** Consult an online catalogue for a university or college that uses the Library of Congress Classification system. Write the call number and title of one source related to each of the following topics.

| Example | Call Number | Title |
|---|---|---|
| **1.** a computer programming book | | |
| **2.** a book on solar energy | | |
| **3.** a novel by Michael Ondaatje | | |
| **4.** a book about the life of Emily Carr | | |
| **5.** a book on Canadian architect Douglas Cardinal | | |

**B.** Complete the following activities to investigate a job sector or career you are interested in pursuing.

**Topic:** _____

1. Create a KWL chart. List information you currently know about this career in the first column. Then, in the second column, list at least three questions you would like to have answered. (For the purposes of this exercise, you can leave the third column blank.)

| What I KNOW | What I WANT to Know | What I LEARNED |
|---|---|---|
| | | |

2. List and describe in your notebook three sources of information about this career that you find during a visit to your school or community library.

3. Suggest a single key word that you could use on the Internet to find answers to your KWL questions.

_____

4. Suggest a way to improve the results of this key-word search using AND, OR, or NOT.

_____

5. Suggest an exact phrase search that you could use to make your search more precise.

_____

6. Locate one source on the Internet that answers some or all of the questions on your KWL chart. Record the URL, as well as what type of Web site it is and the name of its author or publisher. Then, evaluate the site using the criteria below.

Bias: _____

_____

Authority: _____

_____

Accuracy: _____

_____

Timeliness: _____

_____

Scope: _____

_____

7. Choose a paragraph or section from your Internet source and write a paraphrase of it. Include a parenthetical citation or footnote in the format recommended by your teacher. Attach a copy of the original paragraph.

_____

_____

_____

_____

C. **Choose one of the following topics. Find one book, one magazine article, one newspaper article, and one Internet source related to the topic you chose. Write a bibliography in your notebook that includes these four sources, using the format recommended by your teacher.**

**Topics:**     A Canadian writer     An athlete you admire     A city you would like to visit

**Word Origins (A)** ■ Briefly describe the contribution of each of the following languages to modern-day English. Give at least one example of a modern word that is derived from each language.

**1.** Old English _____

_____

**2.** Old Norse _____

_____

**3.** French _____

_____

**4.** Latin and Greek _____

_____

_____

**Word Origins (B)** ■ List four words in modern-day English that have been adopted from languages other than those listed in the preceding activity. If possible, list the language from which each word is derived.

**1.** _____

**2.** _____

**3.** _____

**4.** _____

**Scientific and Technical Vocabulary** ■ Give an example of a technical or scientific word that fits each of the following descriptions.

**1.** Formed from Greek or Latin roots, prefixes, or suffixes

_____

**2.** Formed by combining letters or words to create a new word

_____

**3.** Formed by adding new meaning to an existing word

_____

**Roots, Prefixes, and Suffixes** ■ Write the prefix and its meaning and the root word and its meaning for each of the following. Then, write what part of speech the suffix implies.

**Example: invention = in (in) + venire (come) + tion (noun-forming)**

**1.** dejection = _____ + _____ + _____

**2.** infinity = _____ + _____ + _____

**3.** antibiotic = _____ + _____ + _____

**Canadian Spelling and Commonly Confused Words** ■ Proofread the following sentences, correcting the spelling to conform with Canadian spelling conventions and replacing misused words with correct ones.

**1.** Did the judge except the accused person's defense?

**2.** The attendant at the theater said they don't have anymore seats available, unless we want to sit way up in the gray section.

**3.** So many people have complemented me on my piano playing that I think all those long, boring practises have paid off.

**Figurative Language** ■ Identify the figure of speech in each of the following sentences as simile, metaphor, personification, paradox, or hyperbole.

**1.** The closer I get to my goal, the further away it seems. _____

**2.** My computer is so old it's got hieroglyphics on the keyboard instead of letters. _____

**3.** After sleeping all night on the hard ground, I felt like the Tin Woodman in the *Wizard of Oz*. _____

**4.** A full, white moon gazed down protectively on the sleeping children. _____

**5.** We were on an urban safari, hacking our way through the downtown jungle. _____

**Subjects and Predicates** ■ Underline the complete subject once and the complete predicate twice in the following sentences. If the subject is implied, underline only the complete predicate.

1. Kezia and her friends on the Yearbook Committee worked hard to produce a really professional-looking book.

2. The Ottawa Senators played well, but were eliminated in the third round of the playoffs.

3. There were too many people in the fishing boat.

4. Please don't tell Tawan about the surprise party.

5. Neither the Coast Guard nor the search-and-rescue team could reach the sinking ship.

**Direct and Indirect Objects and Subject Complements** ■ Identify the word in each sentence that fits the description in parentheses and underline it twice. Underline words that modify that word once.

1. Because I was late, I missed the beginning of the movie. (direct object)

2. Sylvie was the team's lead scorer overall. (subject complement)

3. On Sunday, I invited over all my friends. (direct object)

4. Vera wrote Ty a letter to congratulate him. (indirect object)

5. My mother always makes my brothers and me lasagna on our birthdays. (indirect object)

**Sentence Structure** ■ Label each of the following sentences as simple (S), compound (CP), complex (CX), or compound–complex (CC).

1. A beachcomber is someone who salvages logs that break loose from log booms. _____

2. After the barbecue exploded, the party ended quickly. _____

3. Take the subway to save yourself some time. _____

4. When you leave, please close the door or the cat will escape. _____

5. I will accept your apology, but you must promise never to do it again. _____

**Adjective, Adverb, and Noun Clauses** ■ Underline the subordinate clause in each sentence. Identify its function in the sentence as **ADJ** for adjective, **ADV** for adverb, or **N** for noun.

1. Hold on to your paddle, because we are coming to a tricky part of the river. _____

2. What you do tells more about you than your clothes or your ideas. _____

3. People who live in glass houses shouldn't throw stones. _____

4. How that beetle got into the milk bottle is a mystery. _____

5. When he talks, people listen. _____

**Sentence Variety** ■ Identify the sentences that are in inverted order by writing **I** on the line. Then, write **L** for loose or **P** for periodic to describe the remaining sentences.

1. Moving like a whirlwind, a dustpan in one hand and a broom in the other, Karl quickly tidied his room.

   _____

2. Across the schoolyard, with a grim look on her face, marched the principal. _____

3. Did anybody pick up a blue bag like this one by mistake? _____

4. There was a wall of fire between me and my only escape route. _____

5. The room looked a mess after the party, with chairs overturned, chips ground into the carpet, and paper

   cups and plates strewn everywhere. _____

**Sentence Errors** ■ Identify the sentence error in each sentence as **RO** for run-on, **CS** for comma splice, or **SF** for sentence fragment.

1. Let's eat before we go the airline doesn't offer meals. _____

2. Sailing off, with the wind at our backs and the great, green ocean before us. _____

3. I suppose you think that was funny, I don't. _____

4. Which dessert: frozen yogurt or ice cream? _____

5. I need to stop at the store we are out of sugar. _____

 **Final Review**

## Nouns, Verbs, Modifiers, and Pronouns ■ Choose the correct form of the word in parentheses.

1. Those shoes fit you just (perfect, perfectly)!

2. Our two (dogs, dog's, dogs') bowls are kept at opposite ends of the kitchen.

3. (Whose, Who's) coming to my house after school?

4. I'd like to work for someone (who, whom) I respect.

5. As for (me, myself), I would rather walk than jog.

6. Someone on the girls' hockey team left (her, their) equipment in the locker room.

7. Either Emily or Maanav (is, are) going to feed our cat while we are away.

8. Any owner who leaves a dog in a hot car (doesn't, don't) deserve to own a pet.

9. The Drama Club (is, are) having a meeting at four o'clock.

10. Dave felt (bad, badly) about taking the last slice of pizza.


## Verb Tense ■ Identify the tense of the underlined verb.

1. The plane will have left by the time we get to the airport. _____

2. Anthony was fired for being late too often. _____

3. People have been looking for ways to strike it rich since money was invented. _____

4. Andrea is thinking of moving to Halifax. _____

5. Music has been my passion for the past six years. _____


## Verbal Phrases and Prepositional Phrases ■ Identify each underlined phrase as participial, gerund, infinitive, or prepositional. Then, tell what function (noun, adjective, or adverb) it has in the sentence.

1. People on my street throw a block party once a year. _____

2. Speaking clearly will improve the mark you get on your presentation. _____

3. The audience is starting to laugh. _____

4. Looking very elegant, Tanya descended the staircase. _____

5. To finish the job this week will be next to impossible. _____

**Active and Passive Voice ■ Change each of the following sentences from passive to active voice. If necessary, create a logical subject.**

1. Days after the earthquake, people were still being pulled from the rubble.

2. The space station was constructed by an international team of scientists.

3. Several people are being awarded honorary degrees by the university at this year's convocation.

4. All the food for the party has been prepared in advance by me and my friends.

5. The city's centennial will be celebrated by local groups in many different ways.

**Double Negatives, Misplaced and Dangling Modifiers, and Parallel Structure ■ Rewrite the following sentences to eliminate errors.**

1. We should leave either now, or we should wait until after supper.

2. Racing against the clock, the explosives were defused by the bomb squad.

3. Walking through the park, someone grabbed my purse.

4. Approaching the base of the falls in the boat, we couldn't hardly see because of all the sea spray.

5. Kiefer watched as the calf was born with tears in his eyes.

**Commas** ■ **Circle any unnecessary commas in the following sentences.**

1. The report, which was prepared by the United Nations, claims that, the supply of fresh, clean drinking water is dwindling, and will probably continue to decline.

2. "Nanotechnology is, the future of engineering," the speaker proclaimed.

3. John's approach, which sounds sensible to me, is, to study a little every night for a week before the test.

4. When you live in Rankin Inlet, you know, what winter is all about.

5. The acting was, convincing, passionate, and entertaining.

**Semicolons and Colons** ■ **In the sentences that follow, change existing punctuation to semicolons or colons where necessary, and insert semicolons or colons where they are needed.**

1. Because of my allergies, I have to avoid three things, dogs, ragweed, and wheat.

2. Every spring, I spend my time indoors with a red nose, however, I usually feel better as soon as hay-fever season is over.

3. Barbecuing it's the great Canadian summer sport.

4. I introduced Ted to my mother, Valerie, my sister, Julie, and my cat, Harvey.

5. The minister made a statement, "The department is doing everything in its power to ensure the best interests of the public are being served."

**Punctuating Quotations** ■ **Add missing punctuation to the following sentences.**

1. Mr. Coldwell asked____Would you like to join us for lunch____

2. ___Team____said the supervisor____it's time for us to get to work____

3. ____Watch out____yelled the guide.

4. My grandfather always said____Home is where the heart is____however, as a young man he travelled around the world.

5. Which famous hockey legend was known as____The Pocket Rocket____

**Ellipses, Square Brackets, and Single Quotation Marks** ■ Revise the quotations by adding ellipses, square brackets, and single quotation marks as needed. Refer to the original quotation in the box that follows.

> Glenn Gould used to talk about "the idea of North" as it affects Canadians. I think Glenn was right about this. It pervades Canadian thinking. It's a tough land, and we get good at what we do, because the emptiness at our backs and the concomitant dark winter threats are never far from our thoughts.
> —from *Oscar Peterson: The Will to Swing* by Gene Lees

1. Gene Lees explains, "Glenn Gould used to talk about the idea of North that pervades Canadian thinking."

_____

_____

2. Lees muses that "Canada is a tough land, and the emptiness at our backs and the concomitant dark winter threats are never far from our thoughts."

_____

_____

**Punctuating Titles** ■ Add underlining or quotation marks to the titles in the following sentences.

1. Carol Shields' novel Unless was a bestseller.

2. The article War and Roses in Maclean's magazine contains a report by Alexandre Trudeau on the fall of Baghdad in 2003.

3. Have you seen the classic sci-fi movie Invasion of the Body Snatchers?

**Apostrophes and Hyphens** ■ Add apostrophes and hyphens where necessary in the sentences that follow.

1. My sixty five year old uncle has a third degree black belt.

2. Pasta is Jims favourite quick n easy supper.

3. My 91 Honda Civics got a rust speckled body, but the engines still better than yours is.

4. I couldnt see the stage, but if the crowds oohs and ahs were any indication, the black light theatre show was awesome.

5. Im gettin tired of that self involved artist who sings hurtin songs!

# MLA Style

The following gives a simplified version of some basic features of the MLA style of documenting sources. For details, check *The MLA Handbook for Writers of Research Papers*.

## IN-TEXT CITATIONS
- When quoting, paraphrasing, or summarizing another person's ideas, include enough information in parentheses **after the reference but before the end punctuation** for the reader to locate the complete source in your bibliography. Usually, the author's surname and a page number is sufficient.
- **Do not repeat information** that has already been noted in the body of the text.
- If the document has no page or section numbers (for example, if it is an online source), **use the the author's name** alone.
- If the document has no author, **use a word from the title** to identify it.

    EXAMPLES:

    One writer points out that money and the desire for independence are the prime motivating factors for young people looking for their first job (Schaffer 7).

    As Karen Schaffer writes in Hire Power, "I can muse all I like about happiness, skills, and career opportunities, but the truth of the matter is that many of us would never get a job if we didn't need the money" (7).

## BIBLIOGRAPHY
- MLA style uses the heading **Works Cited**, centred at the top of the page.
- Entries should be **double-spaced** and **listed alphabetically by author** (if no author is given, use the title).
- All lines except the first line of each entry should be **indented five spaces**.

## Book with one author
Schaffer, Karen. Hire Power: The Ultimate Job Guide for

   Young Canadians. Toronto: Prentice-Hall Canada, 1997.

## Book with two authors
James, Peter, and Nick Thorpe. Ancient Inventions.

   New York: Ballantine, 1994.

## Book with no author
Language Power Book J. Toronto: Gage Learning

   Corporation, 2004.

## Book with an editor
Halpern, Daniel, ed. The Art of the Story: An International

   Anthology of Contemporary Short Stories.

   New York: Penguin, 1999.

## One piece in a collection or anthology
Mukherjee, Bharati. "The Management of Grief." The Art of

   the Story: An International Anthology of Contemporary

   Short Stories. Ed. Daniel Halpern. New York: Penguin,

   1999. 435–47.

## Magazine article
**Note:** For weekly or daily magazines, write the date as you would for a newspaper article (e.g., 9 Mar. 2002). For seasonal magazines, write the season and the year (e.g., Spring 2002).

Hampson, Sarah. "Lady of the House." Toronto Life Dec.

   2002: 109.

## Newspaper article
**Note:** Use the + symbol only if the article appears on several pages that are not in sequence.

Whittington, Les. "Boom in Jobs Heralds Rebound."

   Saturday Star 9 Mar. 2002, Ont. ed.: A1+.

## Video
**Note:** If you are citing the work of an actor or director, begin the entry with his or her name, followed by the title.

The Grey Fox. Dir. Phillip Borsos. Perf. Richard Farnsworth

   and Jackie Burroughs. Videocassette. Media Home

   Entertainment, 1983.

## Web pages
**Note:** The first date listed is the date the article or information was posted (if available). The second date is the date when it was retrieved from the site by the user. Use angled brackets around URL addresses.

Mah, Bill. "City's Hand-Held Cellphone Ban Placed on

   Hold." Edmonton Journal 4 Apr. 2002. 5 Apr. 2002

   <http://www.canada.com/edmonton/edmontonjournal/

   story.asp?id={2F8F947D-F919-4227-A371-

   7594D518BA45}>.

# APA Style

The following gives a simplified version of some basic features of the APA style of documenting sources. For details, check the *Publication Manual of the American Psychological Association*.

## IN-TEXT CITATIONS
- The basic citation should include the **author's surname and initials,** the **year of publication** and the **page number** (with the abbreviation p. or pp.), separated by commas.
- **Do not repeat information** that has already been noted in the body of the text.
- In citations of works with no page numbers, **include only the author's last name** (or the name of the organization if there is no author given) **and the publication date.**

  EXAMPLES:

  One writer points out that money and the desire for independence are the prime motivating factors for young people looking for their first job (Schaffer, 1997, p. 7).

  As Karen Schaffer writes in her 1997 book, *Hire Power,* "I can muse all I like about happiness, skills, and career opportunities, but the truth of the matter is that many of us would never get a job if we didn't need the money" (p. 7).

## BIBLIOGRAPHY
- APA style uses the heading **References**, centred at the top of the page.
- Entries should be **double-spaced** and **listed alphabetically by author** (if no author is given, use the title).
- The first line of each entry should be **indented five spaces**, with all following lines flush left.
- APA references use only the initial(s) of the author.
- Only the first word of the title (and the first word of any subtitle) begins with a capital letter.

## Book with one author
Schaffer, K. (1997). *Hire power: The ultimate job guide for young Canadians.* Toronto: Prentice-Hall Canada.

## Book with two authors
James, P., & Thorpe, N. (1994). *Ancient inventions.* New York: Ballantine.

## Book with no author
*Language Power Book J.* (2004). Toronto: Gage Learning Corporation.

## Book with an editor
Halpern, D. (Ed.). (1999). *The art of the story: An international anthology of contemporary short stories.* New York: Penguin.

## One piece in a collection or anthology
Mukherjee, B. (1999). The management of grief. In D. Halpern (Ed.), *The art of the story: An international anthology of contemporary short stories* (pp. 435–447). New York: Penguin.

## Magazine article
**Note:** For weekly or daily magazines, write the date as you would for a newspaper article (e.g., 2002, March 9). For seasonal magazines, write the season and the year as follows: (2002, Spring)

Hampson, S. (2002, December). Lady of the house. *Toronto Life*, p. 109.

## Newspaper article
**Note:** Write the page numbers separated by a comma only if the article appears on several pages that are not in sequence.

Whittington, L. (2002, March 9). Boom in jobs heralds rebound. *Saturday Star* (Ontario edition) pp. A1, A12.

## Video
Borsos, P. (Director). (1983). *The Grey Fox* [Motion picture]. Canada: Media Home Entertainment.

## Web pages
Mah, W. (2002, April 4). City's hand-held cellphone ban placed on hold. *Edmonton Journal*. Retrieved April 5, 2002, from http://www.canada.com/edmonton/edmontonjournal/story.asp?id={2F8F947D-F919-4227-A371-7594D518BA45}

# Footnotes and Endnotes (MLA Style)

The following gives a simplified version of some basic features of the MLA style for footnote and endnote documentation. For details, check *The MLA Handbook for Writers of Research Papers*.

## FOOTNOTES

- The information in a footnote is essentially the same as that in a bibliography entry. However, page numbers in a footnote or endnote refer specifically to the pages where the quotation or idea is found, as they would in an in-text citation.

- Footnotes begin at the bottom of the page, **four lines below the last line of text**. Each footnote should appear on the same page as the passage it refers to. **Single-space within each footnote**, but **double-space between two footnotes** on the same page. The first line of each entry should be **indented five spaces**, with all subsequent lines of the entry aligned at the left margin.

## ENDNOTES

- Endnotes contain the same information as footnotes and are set up in a similar format. However, endnotes are **double-spaced both within and between notes**.

- Endnotes go on a separate page at the end of the paper, with the heading **Notes** centred at the top of the page.

- Once you have given a full reference for a source, subsequent footnote or endnote references only need to include the last name of the author and the page numbers.

  EXAMPLE:
  [8] Schaffer 244–45.

**Note:** The following samples are formatted as footnotes. As endnotes, they would be double-spaced.

## Book with one author
[1] Schaffer, Karen, <u>Hire Power: The Ultimate Job Guide for Young Canadians</u> (Toronto: Prentice-Hall Canada, 1997) 7.

## Book with two authors
[2] Peter James and Nick Thorpe, <u>Ancient Inventions</u> (New York: Ballantine, 1994) 23–35.

## Book with no author
[3] <u>Language Power Book J</u> (Toronto: Gage Learning Corporation, 2004), p. 139.

## Book with an editor
[4] Daniel Halpern, ed., <u>The Art of the Story: An International Anthology of Contemporary Short Stories</u> (New York: Penguin, 1999).

## One piece in a collection or anthology
[5] Bharati Mukherjee, "The Management of Grief," <u>The Art of the Story: An International Anthology of Contemporary Short Stories</u>, ed. Daniel Halpern (New York: Penguin, 1999) 435–47.

## Magazine article
[6] Sarah Hampson, "Lady of the House," <u>Toronto Life</u> Dec. 2002: 109.

## Newspaper article
[7] Les Whittington, "Boom in Jobs Heralds Rebound," <u>Saturday Star</u>, 9 Mar. 2002, Ont. ed.: A1.

## Video
[8] <u>The Grey Fox</u>, dir. Phillip Borsos, perf. Richard Farnsworth and Jackie Burroughs, Videocassette, Media Home Entertainment, 1983.

## Web pages
**Note:** The first date listed is the date the article or information was posted (if available). The second date is the date when it was retrieved from the site by the user. Use angled brackets around URL addresses.

[9] Brian D. Johnson, "A Prophet Gets Some Honour," <u>Maclean's</u> 2 Dec. 2002, 6 May 2003 <http://www.macleans.ca/xtadoc2/2002/12/02/Media/76011.shtml>.

# Index